Margaret Thornby's guide to

Tea Rooms
of Britain

D0320468

Published by
Whitehill Publishing
2 Ennel Copse
North Baddesley
Southampton
Hampshire
SO52 9LB

© **Whitehill Publishing July 1998**

ISBN 0 9525838-2-8

Printed by: Solutions Print Management

My grateful thanks to the following for their support,
assistance and patience:-

Sue and John Heaps
Ann Levey
Chris Richards
Richard Eade
Margaret Teagle

Who all helped in making this happen.

M.T.

Margaret Thornby's guide to
Tea Rooms of Britain

Welcome to the second edition of Margaret Thornby's guide to Tea Rooms of Britain!

I wrote the first guide because I adore afternoon tea. Not just for the tea (though Earl Grey with a little milk is my favourite) but the whole experience. A perfectly brewed cup of tea, taken in pleasant surroundings with a home baked scone, a freshly made sandwich, a slice of home made cake, is just heavenly! While afternoon tea at home, taken on the lawn or in the conservatory, is enjoyable, only a traditional tea shop can provide the perfect setting. I also wish for people to share my passion, hence this guide.

In my second edition, many of the establishments featured in the first edition are updated and extended, and several new ones have been introduced. Each tea room is unique, and it is my hope that there is something to suit each and every one of you!

I trust that you enjoy sampling this selection of tea rooms as much I have enjoyed collecting them.

M.T.

TEA, A POEM

While Bards renown'd dine Feat of Arms rehearse
No hostile deeds prophane my milder Verse
From boisterous Ward my Lays entircly free,
The sweet resistless Force of gentle tea.

Thy Power rever'd o'er num'rous Realms is known
and half the willing world appears thine own
In China fix'd thy throne, her sons renown'd
In Arts adore thee and thy worth resound

Glad Europe's fair Daughters catch the flying Fame
and raise a thousand Altars to thy Name!
Thy gifts they taste, and while they taste they prise
Nor envy Jove the Nectar of the skies!

(Aaron Ward)

Contents

The area covered by this book has been divided into eight regions, composed as follows:

1) Scotland
2) North West - Cheshire, Cumbria, Lancashire, Merseyside
3) North East - Durham, Northumberland, Yorkshire, Tyne & Wear
4) Midlands - Derbyshire, Gloucestershire, Hereford & Worcester, Leicestershire, Northamptonshire, Nottinghamshire, Shropshire, Staffordshire, West Midlands, Warwickshire.
5) Wales
6) Eastern Counties - Cambridgeshire, Essex, Lincolnshire, Norfolk, Suffolk
7) South East - Bedfordshire, Berkshire, Buckinghamshire, East Sussex, West Sussex, Hampshire & Isle of Wight, Hertfordshire, Kent, Oxfordshire, Surrey.
8) South West - Cornwall, Devon, Dorset, Somerset, Wiltshire, Avon.

i) The tea rooms are identified initially by the region they are in, and within each region, in alphabetical order by town or village. Refer to the back of the book for indexes by tea room name and town or village.
ii) Parking facilities are identified in three ways; parking on the premises, within 50 metres or within 100 metres, to assist guests in reaching the tea shop of their choice as easily as possible.
iii) Access for the disabled is noted where available. In some instances, assistance may be required for disabled people to access the premises, and this is pointed out in the text.
iv) Prices, where mentioned, were correct at the time of going to press.

Scotland

Calums Tearoom

21 Commerce Street   Disabled Access
Arbroath   Parking - within 50m
Angus
DD11 1NA   Tel: 01241 431229

Calum's Tearooms are "like tea rooms used to be" in the words of proprietors Benita O'Reilly and James McLean. Elegantly designed menus reminiscent of the 1920s complement the peach wallpaper and matching tablecloths. The flowered china and grandfather clock combine to make a tea room where regulars and visitors return again and again. Glen Miller music plays quietly in the background or the pianist plays Gershwin classics, while waitresses in traditional uniforms bring the home made food to the tables.

The tearoom is located off the High Street and close to the Webster Theatre, Arbroath Abbey, the Harbour with 'smokie' shops and there are cliff walks to the north of Arbroath.

Calums specialises in some wonderful teas - Calums House Teas, Ceylon Teas, Indian Teas, China Teas, Formosa Teas and a splendid range of herbal infusions. Also available are herbal fruit teas, coffee from the Edinburgh Coffee Company and a selection of cold drinks.

All dishes on their menu are prepared, wherever possible, using the finest locally produced goods, and include smoked salmon scramble for High Tea, sandwiches, home baked goods, tea or coffee for Traditional Tea, or for Cream Tea, two scones with butter, preserves and whipped cream and a pot of tea or coffee.

Hours of business:
Mondays to Fridays - 9.30am to 5pm
Saturdays - 9.30am to 6pm
Closed on Sundays.

Station Tea Room & Craft Shop

Station Square   Disabled Access
Dingwall   Parking - within 50m
Ross-shire
IV15 9JD   Tel: 01349 865894

Part of Dingwall Railway Station, the Tea Room and Craft Shop is a wonderful welcome to the attractive small market town which offers a good range of shops to its visitors.

The Station itself is a listed building, built in 1886 for the Highland Railway. About half the building, including the former waiting rooms, have been transformed into an attractive tea room and quality gift shop, which sells many items made by local craftspeople.

The local baker bakes the bread, but cakes, scones and jams are all home made. Afternoon Tea serves a pot of tea with a scone, jam and butter. Freshly brewed teas include Assam, Ceylon, China, Darjeeling and Earl Grey.

Home made soups are a speciality and light lunches are served.

Hours of business:
Summer - Mondays to Saturdays 10am to 5pm
Winter - Mondays to Saturdays 10am to 4pm.

Kind Kyttock's Kitchen

Cross Wynd   Disabled Access
Falkland   Parking - within 50m
Fife
KY15 7BE   Tel: 01337 857477

Situated beside the village green in the heart of a conservation village, Kind Kyttock's Kitchen, which was opened in 1970, is named after the heroine in Dunbar's poem, who provided hospitality for weary travellers. Part of the building dates back to 1712, some of the original features having been retained to give atmosphere to the tea room, which is pleasant and friendly.

Kind Kyttock's Kitchen's reputation for quality food is known throughout the world and the aim of Bert and Liz Dalrymple, the proprietors, is to offer good food which is nutritious, appetising and freshly prepared. It is recommended by Egon Ronay and a member of the "Guild of Tea Shops" and the "Taste of Scotland" scheme.

The menu itself is a beautifully presented booklet which contains not only a list of the fare available, but also some very interesting information and the Ballad of Kind Kyttock.

Choose between the Cream Tea, or the Afternoon Tea, which includes a choice of home made traditional Scot's pancakes or home made scones. Without doubt, you will be spoilt for choice here, especially with the array of wonderful home baked cakes, such as millionaire shortbread, ginger oatie, Campbell fudge cake and braw wee meringue.

Hours of business:
Daily - 10.30am to 5.30pm.
Closed Mondays
Closed Christmas Eve until 5th January.

Abbey Cottage
26 Main Street   Disabled Access
New Abbey   Parking - on premises
Dumfries
DG2 8BY   Tel: 01387 850377

In the picturesque conservation village of New Abbey, next to the historic ruin of Sweetheart Abbey lies Abbey Cottage. This Victorian cottage is tastefully furnished in Laura Ashley, with pastel tablecloths. Intricate samplers cover the walls, sewn by proprietor Morag McKie and her daughters. French doors lead to a terrace next to the Abbey itself.

Healthy, delicious food is served in a non-smoking atmosphere and free range eggs and local produce are used in the cooking, much of which is done by Jacqui Wilson, Morag's daughter and her fellow proprietor.

Meals are freshly prepared and made to order. While there is no set menu, cakes, gingerbread, shortbread and fruit loaves offer a tempting selection, with carrot cake highly recommended and the jams full of home grown fruit.

Assam, Lemon, Darjeeling and Earl Grey teas are served in white china. Alternatively, there is a selection of speciality coffees and herbal infusions. The standards at Abbey Cottage gained it membership of the Tea Council's Guild of Tea Shops and entries in two of Egon Ronay's guides.

Hours of business:
1st April to 31st October - 7 days a week 10am to 5.30pm.
November & December - weekends only 11am to 5pm.
Closed from Christmas to end of March.

North West

Aunty Val's Tea Rooms

Church Street
Bowness on Windermere
Cumbria
LA23 3DG

Disabled Access
Parking - within 100m

Tel: 01539 488211

Situated behind the ancient church of St Martins, in the heart of beautiful Bowness. Not far away are Lake Windermere, the pier for the Lake steamer and the Beatrix Potter Exhibition. Whatever the time of year, this is a wonderfully scenic place to visit!

The tea rooms are set in a listed building overlooking the church and inside the Laura Ashley décor and collection of tea pots and memorabilia combine to give a quaint and welcoming atmosphere.

Guests can choose from an array of sandwiches, snacks, cakes and pastries. There are seasonal specials but sticky toffee pudding, chocolate fudge cake and carrot cake are hard to resist! For the hungry walkers the Cumberland pie is sure to satisfy.

Teas available include Superior Ceylon Tea, or a range of Exotic teas including Ceylon, Earl Grey, Darjeeling, Lapsang, and several herbal teas and infusions. Lakeland Gifts are on sale in the Tea Rooms, such as boxes of Kendal Mint Cake, Clotted Cream Fudge that come with a drawing of the Tea Rooms, or luxury preserves and gift tins of tea.

Hours of business:
Open seven days a week all year round 11am to 5pm
Closed Fridays in winter season.

Astbury Tea Shop
Astbury Marsh   Disabled Access
Congleton   Parking - on premises
Cheshire
CW12 4HS   Tel: 01260 277099

Located within a couple of minutes walk of the historic village of Astbury
and five minutes drive of Congleton, Astbury Tea Shop is ideally situated
for cyclists and walkers. This peaceful haven is close to the local
attractions of Little Moreton Hall and the Astbury Country Park.

Astbury Tea Shop has been praised not only for the quality of the food and
drink, but also its friendliness, and in summer the garden is an extension
of the tea room, with tables and benches on the lawns which are
surrounded by shrubs and flower beds. Enjoy the soothing music that is
quietly played whilst you sample the fare.

Food, wholly prepared and cooked on the premises, includes baked
potatoes, quiches (including vegetarian options) and freshly prepared
sandwiches. Cream Tea, for a reasonable £3.65, provides a sandwich of
your choice with salad garnish, a home made scone, jam and cream and a
pot of tea or coffee.

Several varieties of home made cakes and fruit pies are on offer, such as
date and walnut, cherry coconut madeira, rich fruit cake, and strawberry
gateau in season. To quench the thirst are a choice of teas, including China
and Earl Grey.

Hours of business:
January to November - Saturdays to Thursdays (closed on Fridays).

Marjory's Tea Room
65 Blackburn Road
Darwen   Parking - within 50m
Lancashire
BB3 1EJ   Tel: 01254 776587

A cosy atmosphere and friendly service is offered by proprietor Marjory Harrison to all her customers, who might also enjoy a browse around her husband's second hand/antique shop downstairs.

Cakes and scones are all home baked, and the absence of a set menu allows for a greater choice among the very reasonably priced goodies. Freshly cut sandwiches and special toasties tempt those who prefer their savouries, and traditional scones with jam and cream are available for the sweet toothed. Earl Grey is a favourite tea on offer.

Hours of business:
Open daily except Sundays and Mondays.

––– oOo –––––––

Now stir the fire and close the shutters fast,
Let fall the curtains, wheel the sofa round,
And, while the bubbling and loud hissing urn
Throws up a steamy column, and the cups,
That cheer but not inebriate, wait on each,
So let us welcome peaceful evening in.

(William Cowper)

Lantern Tea Rooms
30 Kent Road   Disabled Access
Fleetwood   Parking - within 50m
Lancashire
FY7 6AF   Tel: 01253 874418

Lantern Tea Rooms sits alongside the tramtracks from Fleetwood to
Blackpool and close to Fleetwood market, a lovely promenade and the Isle
of Man ferry. The tea rooms are set in an old building with seating for
about thirty outside on the patio during good weather.

Afternoon Tea offers a toasted teacake, a scone with jam and cream and a
pot of tea per person. Cakes and scones are all home baked and there is a
good selection to choose from, including fruit pies and egg custards.
Among the teas available are Assam, Ceylon, China, Darjeeling and Earl
Grey.

Hours of business:
Closed on Wednesdays.

——— oOo ———

*Wouldn't it be dreadful to live in a
country where they didn't serve tea?*

(Noel Coward)

The Cottage Tea Shop

121 Main Street   Disabled Access

Frodsham   Parking - within 50m

Cheshire

WA6 7AF   Tel: 01928 733673

The Cottage Tea Shop is set in the town centre near to the Castle Park Arts Centre. The very old building has a low, beamed ceiling and lace tablecloths, bone china and lots of fresh flowers give a traditional ambience. Children are welcome, with colouring books, high chairs and training cups available on request. The toilet facilities are spotless.

Cream Tea consists of a choice of one or two freshly baked scones, jam, cream and tea or coffee. Afternoon Tea offers a choice of sandwich, a scone with the trimmings and a slice of cake. Cakes, scones and jams are home made and the teas on offer include Assam, Darjeeling and Earl Grey.

Home made jams and marmalade may be purchased. There is also a Specials Board with hot and cold meals such as hot pot, quiche, fresh salmon sandwiches and tuna pasta - all home made. Delicious!

Hours of business:

Daily - 10am to 4.30pm.

Closed Wednesdays and Sundays.

Hillcrest Tea Rooms
Mitton Road   Disabled Access
Great Mitton   Parking - on premises
Nr Clitheroe
Lancashire
BB7 9PQ   Tel: 01254 826573

Hillcrest Tea Rooms are set in a small hamlet next to the medieval church, which was built during the reign of Edward III, and are not far from the famous public school, Stoneyhurst College. Local attractions include historical buildings such as Whalley Abbey.

The old building has a cheerful, relaxed atmosphere in a quiet, tranquil setting, with friendly staff serving at lace covered tables. There is a beautiful garden at the side of the medieval church.

Scones and cakes are all home made and the home grown fruit is made into pies and delicious jams. There is no set menu, to allow the customers a wider choice for their afternoon tea.

Parkin and sticky toffee pudding are among the house specialities, and the range of teas include Assam, China, Darjeeling and Earl Grey. Fresh ground coffee is also available. Hot meals are served from 12 noon until 4.30pm.

Hours of business:
Mondays to Wednesdays - 10am to 4.45pm
Saturdays and Sundays - 10am to 4.45pm.
Closed on Thursdays and Fridays.

Dorothy's Tea Shoppe
72 Chestergate
Macclesfield   Parking - within 100m
Cheshire
SK11 6DY   Tel: 01625 503733

Situated above Gate House Antiques, Dorothy's Tea Shoppe is part of an old beamed building. It is not far from the Heritage Centre with the Silk Museum and various old schools and churches.

Dorothy herself is the proprietor, presenting tea to her guests on Eternal Beau tea service. Very reasonably priced Cream Tea offers a home baked scone with jam, cream and tea.

There is a choice of other home made produce; lemon meringue pie, carrot cake and Bakewell tart, and Earl Grey is the speciality tea. Guests can purchase a cloth made "Dorothy" bag, available in a variety of sizes and colours, as a souvenir of their visit.

Hours of business:
Daily - 8.30am to 5pm
Closed Wednesdays and Sundays.

——— oOo ———

There is a great deal of poetry and fine sentiment in a chest of tea.

(Emerson)

The Village Bakery
Melmerby   Disabled Access
Penrith   Parking - within 50m
Cumbria
CA10 1PT   Tel: 01768 881515

The 200 year old converted stone barn overlooks the picturesque village green, with the Pennine hills in the background. Located on the A686 between Penrith and Alston, the surrounding scenery is superb, and draws walkers and drivers alike.

The restaurant shop sells a full range of Village Bakery products including fresh bread, cakes, biscuits, puddings, jams and a range of home baking equipment. Much of the excellent produce is grown on the five acre small holding behind the bakery, and Village Bakery breads are sold in several food shops around the country, such as Waitrose, Fenwicks and EH Booth & Co. A very extensive mail order service, Village Bakery Direct, is available to customers to allow you to sample the delicious fare from your home.

The menu itself is full of imaginative specialities; for example, sandwiches such as bacon & avocado on sunflower bread or smoked trout on Borodinsky bread, all home made. For afternoon tea, the menu is similarly imaginative, with healthy and delicious treats such as organic simnel cake, organic cheese scone with butter or Grasmere gingerbread! Fine loose leaf speciality teas are served, along with a range of unusual soft drinks including home made lemonade. A very special place for your afternoon tea!

Hours of business:
Mondays to Saturdays - 8.30am to 5pm
Sundays - 9.30am to 5pm.

Abbey Tea Room
Abbey Stores & Tea Room   Disabled Access
Rosedale Abbey   Parking - within 50m
Nr Pickering
North Yorkshire
YO18 8SA   Tel: 01751 417475

The pretty blue and primrose Laura Ashley tea room, opposite the village church, has picture windows overlooking the village green. During the iron mining boom of the early 20th century, the site was part of a large store, supplying everything from sacks of flour to clothing.

Yorkshire Cream Tea serves a scone with strawberry jam, whipped cream, home made cake and a pot of tea. Abbey Special Tea comprises salmon and cucumber sandwiches, a scone and a pot of tea.

Sandwiches are freshly made and cakes and scones home baked. Ginger scone with ginger jam and cream, or apricot and cheese gateau are just a couple of the mouthwatering choices on the menu. Teas include Ceylon, Darjeeling and Earl Grey.

Hours of business:
Easter to end of October - 10.30am to 5.30pm (closed on Wednesdays).

Nostalgia Tea Room
215-217 Lord Street
Southport   Parking - within 50m
Merseyside
PR8 1NZ   Tel: 01704 501294

Nostalgia by name and nature, the listed building which houses the Tea Rooms was built in half-timbered black and white style. The Tea Rooms are on the first floor; from window tables you can watch the world go by on Lord Street, a Victorian canopied arcade.

Inside, there is a light and spacious feel to the room, which has a distinctive peach and green décor, with personally designed bamboo furniture. Locally, visitors can enjoy the good shopping, the promenade gardens and golf at the Royal Birkdale.

The Nostalgia Tea Rooms are well known for their home made meals and soups as well as gaining some local fame for their home made scones and cakes.

The possibilities for tea include Cream Teas, Afternoon Tea, Special Afternoon Tea and the Nostalgia Special. Otherwise guests can make their own selections from the delicious foods on the menu.

Hours of business:
Tuesdays to Saturdays - 9.30am to 5pm
Sundays - 10am to 5pm
Closed on Mondays.
Open Bank Holidays 10am to 5pm.

Tiffins Tea Shop
Marsh Mill Village   Disabled Access
Thornton   Parking - on premises
Lancashire

                                                     Tel: 01253 857100

Within the village complex, in the shadow of Thornton Windmill, Tiffins is a purpose built tea room on the edge of the village square. It is well known locally for high quality home baked cakes. Local attractions include the 1794 Museum Windmill, craft shops and entertainments in the Village Square.

The appropriate name 'Tiffins' comes from the colloquialism for tiffing - to take a little drink or sip and was adapted into Anglo-Indian use in India and Eastern countries for taking a light meal.

All the food is freshly prepared ensuring that guests receive quality food, and the beautifully presented menu offers a mouthwatering selection of light lunches, hot meals, toasts, tea breads, salads, and afternoon teas, plus a children's menu. A Tiffins speciality not be missed is the Lancashire Bagging afternoon tea, consisting of two thick slices of Borrowdale Tea Loaf with a chunk of creamy Lancashire cheese and butter, plus hot tea for one. Scrumptious!

A superb range of teas and coffees are on offer, each with an imaginative description on the menu.

Hours of business:
Mondays to Saturdays - 10am to 5pm
Sundays - 11am to 5pm
Last orders for food - 4.30pm.

The Chatteries Tea Rooms

7 Jaxons Court　　　　　　　　　　　　Disabled Access
off Hallgate　　　　　　　　　　　　　Parking - within 100m
Wigan
Lancashire
WN5 1LR　　　　　　　　　　　　　　Tel: 01942 820988

The Chatteries are part of an olde worlde complex to the side of Wigan bus station, in the historic part of the town centre, where visitors can take a look at local heritage and they are not far from the famous Wigan Pier.

The varied menu is suitable for breakfast, lunch and afternoon tea. The Cream Tea offers a scone with cream and preserve and a pot of English Breakfast Tea, and plate salads are a speciality. A hungry customer dines on hot pot with red cabbage or beetroot, a pot of tea or coffee, and a scone or eccles cake. Cakes are all home baked and there is a good choice of high quality teas including Assam, Ceylon, Darjeeling and Earl Grey.

Hours of business:
Mondays to Saturdays - 8.30am to 4.30pm
Sundays - closed.

Oh some are fond of Spanish wine and some are fond of French,
And some'll swallow tay and stuff fit only for a wench.

(John Masefield - Captain Stratton's Fancy)

North East

The Copper Kettle Tea Rooms

21 Front Street   Disabled Access limited
Bamburgh   Parking - within 50m
Northumberland
NE69 7BW   Tel: 01668 214315

Dating from the early 1700s, the stone built cottage has barrelled beamed ceilings and unique hand carved, oak panelled walls depicting local scenes, with antique copperware on display. This venue is set in the historic village of Bamburgh, dominated by its massive pre-12th century castle. There is a museum dedicated to the celebrated Victorian heroine, Grace Darling, who was born in the village and is buried in the local churchyard.

As well as being a member of the prestigious Guild of Tea Shops and Egon Ronay recommended, the tea room has an entry within the "ASH" publication of "Eat, Drink and Sleep Smoke Free", though smokers and dogs are welcome in the patio garden.

There is no set tea menu, but a superb offering of home baked goods, including tea loaf, tiffin, caramel shortbread, gingerbread or cherry madeira cake. Also available are luscious open sandwiches, blueberry filled crepes, jacket potatoes, and an amazing range of thirty teas and coffees.

From the Copper Kettle Tea Rooms gift shop, high class confectionery, biscuits, preserves, hand made cards and exclusive local paintings are available to purchase.

Hours of business:
Seven days a week 10.30am to 5.30pm.
Closed from end October to mid March but open some winter weekends.

The Priest's House
Barden Tower
Nr Skipton   Parking - on premises
North Yorkshire
BD23 6AS   Tel: 01756 720616

Close to Strid Woods, a site of special scientific interest, and Bolton Abbey, the tea rooms lie in the heart of the beautiful Yorkshire Dales, and are located in the 15th century priest's house next to the ruins of Barden Tower. There is disabled access to the tea garden only.

Guests may take tea either outside overlooking the ruins, or in the Oak Room, which takes its name from the oak beamed ceiling and magnificent oak dressers. The dressers house a fine collection of antique willow pattern meat platters, echoed in the crockery used in the tea room. Allow yourself to be soothed by the gentle period background music in the Oak Room.

Lady Anne's Tea offers a dainty sandwich, scone with jam and cream, a slice of Dales flapjack with a pot of tea. The menu includes biscuits, crumpets, pancakes and a daily selection of cakes, puddings and fancies. Sandwiches include Dainties or Doorsteps - absolutely delicious! And on a cold day, try the Tower Broth, a hearty soup served with thick granary bread.

There is an excellent range of speciality teas, fruit and herbal teas, and a range of coffees. If you're looking for a tea room with a truly historic ambience, you will find it here!

Hours of business:
Summer (mid March to end October) open Saturdays to Wednesdays 10.30am to 5pm - closed Thursdays and Fridays
November to 20th December - open weekends only 11am to 4pm
20th December to 2nd January - 11am to 4pm (except Christmas Day)
Closed from 3rd January to mid March.

The Market Place Teashop

29 Market Place   Disabled Access
Barnard Castle   Parking - within 50m
Co Durham
DL12 8NE   Tel: 01833 690110

Situated in the market place, near to the Castle ruins, the River Tees and the Bowes Museum, The Market Place Teashop occupies the ground floor of a building dating back to 1611. Built originally as housing, the building has also been used as a temperance hotel and a gentleman's outfitters in its varied past.

The Market Place Teashop was established twenty seven years ago by its present owners. It has gained a reputation for good food and good service, earning mentions in numerous food guides and an award from the AA and Ty-phoo of 'Tea place of the Year' in 1990.

The menus change daily presenting a range of food and soups made mostly on the premises. Visitors select their own afternoon tea from the tempting range of cakes, scones and speciality teas.

In particular, the range of Italian ice creams containing only natural fruits and flavourings, the peach meringue, and the Ice Cream Extravaganza are naughty but nice!

Hours of business:
Mondays to Saturdays 10.30am to 5.30pm
Sundays 2.30 to 5.30pm.

Clark's Tea Rooms

Market Place   Disabled Access
Easingwold   Parking - within 50m
York
North Yorkshire
YO61 3AG   Tel: 01347 823143

Set on the edge of Herriot country, and close to the scenic North Yorkshire Moors, Clark's Tea Rooms overlook the green from their position in the market square, providing a welcome resting place whilst browsing through the antique shops or the Friday market in this pretty Georgian town.

Inside, pretty pink and green Laura Ashley curtains complement unusual table cloths covered in English and Latin quotations. There are pavement tables to take tea at when the weather permits.

Afternoon Tea consists of a selection of sandwiches, a savoury such as a cornish pasty or sausage roll, cakes, scones, and a pot of tea. Very tasty and very good value for £3.50. Members of the Guild of Tea Shops, proprietors Gerald and Judy Clark also own their own bakery which produces the bread, cakes and pastries served here, and the beef and ham are roasted in the bakehouse ovens. The specialities of Yorkshire Curd Tarts, fruit cake and local Wensleydale cheese are well worth trying.

For a second treat, visit Clark's Café at 195 Long Street, where you will also find their bakery. The theme here reflects the owners' hobby, and is decorated with canal ware, paintings, posters and objets d'art.

Hours of business:
Mondays to Thursdays - 10am to 5pm
Fridays and Saturdays - 9.30am to 5pm
Closed on Sundays.

Gatsby's Tea Rooms
1A Old Market
Halifax   Parking - within 50m
West Yorkshire
HX1 1TN   Tel: 01422 323905

Located opposite the Central Library and close to the open air market and Eureka, the children's museum, Gatsby's Tea Rooms are ideally situated in Halifax town centre. The Old Market was originally built to sell locally made cloth, but now houses various craft shops.

The tea room itself is spacious with good views and serves afternoon tea on Royal Doulton china. Gatsby's is a holder of the 'Roy Castle Heartbeat award for Smoke Free Environment'.

A typical and traditional Cream Tea offers a selection of sandwich triangles, scone with preserve and cream and a home made cake or pastry which are all served on a three tier cake stand, and a pot of Yorkshire tea. There is also a Specials Board which changes daily.

An 'extra special' item is the Weight Watchers daily special where weight watchers points are already worked out. And for the under 12's, there is the Gatsby's Specials menu which features foods with special appeal to children, allowing parents to freely enjoy their delicious Cream Tea!

Hours of business:
Mondays to Fridays - 9.30am to 4.30pm
Saturdays - 9am - 4.30pm
Closed on Sundays.

The Wrinkled Stocking Tea Room

30 Upperbridge   Disabled Access
Holmfirth   Parking - within 50m
West Yorkshire
HD7 1JS   Tel: 01484 681408

This is The Wrinkled Stocking Tea Room seen in the television series "The Last of the Summer Wine" and is often frequented by the cast of the programme. Nora Batty's house is actually next door!

Local attractions include the summer wine exhibition, and the scenery of West Yorkshire.

The Tea Room offers warm and friendly waitress service, with food and sandwiches freshly made to order. Holmfirth Cream Tea offers a pot of tea or coffee with a scone, dish of jam and cream. Afternoon Tea serves a choice of freshly made sandwich with salad garnish, a pot of tea or coffee, and a choice of sweet.

Cakes and scones are all home baked, though not by Nora Batty's fair hand, and include delights such as chocolate fudge cake which is served warm with chocolate sauce and fresh cream, and the range of teas include Yorkshire, Breakfast Blend, Fine Ceylon, Darjeeling and Earl Grey.

Hours of business:
Open all year round seven days a week - 10am to 5pm.
Closed only on Christmas Day.

Dormouse Tea Room
4 Greenbank Road
Mossley Hill   Parking - within 100m
Liverpool
L18 1HN   Tel: 0151 733 7425

The Dormouse Tea Room can be found off the Smithdown Road, opposite the Finch and Furkin Pub. Close by is Sefton Park, the Wavertree Park and Sports Arena, and the famous Penny Lane.

Inside, an old fashioned, traditionally furnished room on the first floor provides a peaceful atmosphere for tea and a bite to eat, whilst being waited on by a uniformed waitress.

Afternoon Tea for two is tea, a sandwich of your choice with a jam and cream scone for £5.40. Other specialities are a range of delicious cakes from Dafnas Cheesecake Factory, and a selection of tasty pies made by Amanda and served with ice cream, cream or custard. Scrumptious!

Teas and coffees by Taylors of Harrogate are served, including Assam, Ceylon, Darjeeling and Earl Grey. The range of coffees is fairly extensive and hot chocolate with cream is also an option. Hot meals, light lunches and filled French sticks are on offer, and for a treat to follow, try the hot chocolate doughnut with cream and ice cream! A children's menu is thoughtfully provided.

Hours of business:
Mondays to Fridays 8.30am to 4pm
Closed on Saturdays and Sundays.

Oulton Hall Hotel
Rothwell Lane   Disabled Access
Oulton   Parking - on premises
Leeds
West Yorkshire
LS26 8HN   Tel: 0113 282 1000

The Grade II listed building is set in exquisite historical gardens, which contain an estimated 30,000 shrubs and plants, as well as 175 exquisite specimen trees, which were designed for the most part by Humphrey Repton.

The Hall itself, of special architectural and historic interest, was initially a simple farmhouse and was rebuilt as a Hall in the 19th century, when it was further extended making it truly a mansion! It has had a variety of uses throughout this century and was acquired for use as a hotel in 1991.

The spectacular Oulton Hall Afternoon Tea is served from 2.30 to 6pm and serves a selection of finger sandwiches, freshly baked scones served with Devon clotted cream and strawberry preserve, dainty French pastries, fruit cake with Wensleydale cheese and your choice from the range of teas or coffees. This is a superb treat at just £7.50 per person! You are advised to contact the Butler to reserve your table for this event.

The menu contains many other delicious items to tempt you, including a range of innovative sandwiches, speciality sandwiches, other home made cakes and biscuits and an excellent range of speciality teas and coffees. A real treat for your Afternoon Tea!

Hours of business:
Open 365 days a year, 10am to 6pm.

The White House
Anvil Square
Reeth   Parking - within 50m
Richmond
North Yorkshire
DL11 6TE   Tel: 01748 884763

Close to the countryside and many local crafts, The White House, located opposite Barclays Bank in Reeth, offers good views and pleasant décor, enhanced by fine bone china at the table. Within easy reach are the breathtaking Yorkshire Dales where a brisk walk will build an appetite for afternoon tea.

There is no set menu, but the variety of cakes, scones and jams are home made, and sandwiches are served with a huge salad. Assam, Darjeeling and Earl Grey are the traditional teas on offer, and there is also a selection of herbal teas.

Hours of business:
Open daily from 10.30am to 4.30pm
Closed Wednesdays and Thursdays.
Closed during February.

——— oOo ———

Nasturtium Leaf Sandwiches

Spread anchovy paste sparingly. Add shredded nasturtium leaves.

(Five O'Clock Tea, 1886)

'Moonraker' Floating Tearoom
Commercial Mills
Slaithwaite   Parking - on premises
Huddersfield
Yorkshire
HD7 5HB   Tel: 01484 846370

Moonraker Floating Tearoom has a distinctive location on board a narrow boat, on the canal between locks 23 and 24. The boat is fitted out in pine, creating a warm, clean atmosphere. Central heating runs through well polished copper pipes and on display are various brass fittings with traditional painted pots and plates, some of which are for sale. The car park is located by the canal, adjacent to Church Lane in the centre of Slaithwaite.

Cakes and biscuits are baked in the galley daily, and there is no set menu for afternoon tea, so there are plenty of options. Hot snacks and home made soups are also available - ideal to warm you on a cold day. In warmer weather, the ice cream floats are delicious! Among the teas are Ceylon - Orange Pekoe, Darjeeling and Earl Grey, with herbal teas Rosehip, Wild Blackcurrant or Camomile.

Hours of business:
Summer -   Tuesdays to Saturdays - 9am to 6pm
                Sundays - 10am to 6pm
                Mondays - closed
Winter -   Mondays and Tuesdays - closed
                Wednesdays to Saturdays - 9am to 4pm
                Sundays - 10am to 4pm
Open all bank holidays.
Closed Christmas Day and Boxing Day.

The Gates Tea Room

29 King Street

Thorne

Doncaster

South Yorkshire

DN8 5AU

Disabled Access

Parking - on premises

Tel: 01405 813634

The Gates Tea Rooms were built in 1700 as the original gate house for carts entering Thorne. After that the building was used as a beer house, then a stonemason's and cobbler's workshop. The tea room is situated on the main road opposite Wilsons Carpet Warehouse, and just one mile from Junction 6 of the M18. Local attractions include the Norman Church and the canal.

Dark wood tables and chairs complement the wooden beams inside to give the impression of bygone ages. The conservatory and the tea garden at the rear are both ideal for the summer. The service is friendly and welcoming, and the atmosphere soothing.

Cream Teas are served by the friendly staff in an olde worlde style. There is no set menu but instead a variety of home made produce is offered. Specialities include scones, chocolate cake, buns and mince pies. Also available are steak, chicken or cheese pies, quiche and assorted omelettes. The favourite tea on offer is Earl Grey.

Hours of business:
Mondays to Saturdays - 9am - 4pm.

The Tearooms
4 Marden Road   Disabled Access
Whitley Bay   Parking - within 50m
Tyne & Wear
NE26 2JH   Tel: 0191 252 3943

This non smoking establishment has been run by Alma and Sidney Heppell since 1987 and is situated near St Paul's Church, close to the Sealife Centre in Marden Quarry in Whitley Bay.

Located just a few miles outside Newcastle upon Tyne, and within easy travelling distance of the Metro Centre at Gateshead. Whitley Bay itself is a well known holiday resort and walks along the beautiful beaches are popular.

Inside, there are two large, well decorated rooms with lovely décor and draped curtains, with pink tablecloths that complement the bone china tableware. In summer it is possible to sit on the patio to enjoy the teas.

There is no set menu, but sandwiches, tea and home made cakes all feature in a reasonably priced selection. Specialities in winter are the sweet mince pies with cream. Fresh fruit flans celebrate the warmer season, meringues are a perennial favourite, and the fruit and cheese scones are baked daily along with the other produce. Teas include Assam, Ceylon, China, Darjeeling and Earl Grey.

Hours of business:
Thursdays to Saturdays - 10am to 4pm
Closed Sundays to Wednesdays.
Open all year.

Betty's Café Tea Rooms
6-8 St Helen's Square   Disabled Access
York
North Yorkshire
YO1 2QP   Tel: 01904 659142

The founder of the Betty's Café Tea Rooms, Frederick Belmont, went on the maiden voyage of the Queen Mary liner in 1936. On his return he decided to base the design of his York café on the liner. It was opened in 1937 and many of the original features still remain. During World War II it was a famous rendezvous for Canadian and RAF airmen.

Downstairs is a mirror with names etched on by those airmen, which is today visited by their relatives. Descendants of the founder still own the business.

The tea rooms are very close to York Minster and other local attractions include the Museum Gardens, the National Railway Museum, Castle Museum, City Walls and the Yorvik Centre.

Cream Tea offers two sultana scones with butter, whipped cream and preserve and a pot of tearoom blend tea. Bread, cakes, scones and jams are all made at Betty's own bakery and specialities include Yorkshire Rarebit, Yorkshire Fat Rascals, Yorkshire Curd Tart and Swiss Rosti.

St Helena coffee is exclusive to Betty's from the island of St Helena, and teas include Assam, Ceylon, China, Darjeeling and Earl Grey.

Hours of business:
Seven days a week - 9am to 9pm.

Midlands

Present Shoppe & Alcester Coffee House

12 High Street   Disabled Access
Alcester   Parking - within 50m
Warwickshire
B49 5AD   Tel: 01789 765126

Set in the middle of the High Street, the Present Shoppe and Alcester Coffee House are found in a Grade II listed building dating from 1642, which makes it the oldest shop in the High Street. Lace tablecloths and bone china add to the historical feel. This is a non smoking establishment, for the comfort of all guests.

Alcester Cream Tea offers a pot of tea or cup of coffee, a delicious home made scone with jam and Cornish clotted cream, and a home baked cake. All cakes are home made, with particular treats being the treacle tart and the Bakewell tart. Cream teas are served all day, and the speciality teas include Earl Grey, Darjeeling, China and Lemon.

Hours of business:
Open Mondays to Saturdays - 10am to 5pm
Closed on Tuesdays.
Sundays - 12 noon to 5pm.

Goose Green Tea Rooms
Nether End   Disabled Access
Baslow   Parking - within 50m
Derbyshire
DE45 1SR   Tel: 01246 583000

Goose Green Tea Rooms overlook Baslow's Goose Green and are next to the village car park, with attractions nearby including Chatsworth House and Park.

The tea rooms live up to their name with the predominantly green décor, the selection of goosey gifts and a large selection of limited edition Derbyshire pictures. The Tea Rooms were Highly Recommended by the Good Café Guide 1988, winners of the 'Loo of the Year' award for two years running, and ITV featured the tea rooms in the series Peak Practice. Large picture windows let guests watch the world go by, after which scenic walks can be taken over the famous Gritstone Edges.

With a No Smoking policy, proprietors John and Margaret Smith pride themselves on a clean environment and friendly service.

The premises are licenced and there is an extensive range of home made fare, with speciality banana and poppy seed cake, cream topped carrot cake, butter shortcake, date and apple pie and fruit custard crumbles. Teas include Assam, Ceylon, Darjeeling and Earl Grey.

Hours of business:
Open daily - all year round:
Weekdays - 9.30am - 5pm
Weekends - 9.30am - 5.30pm

Goose Green Tea Rooms, Baslow

Old Coach House Tearooms
Post Office Square   Disabled Access
Blockley   Parking - on premises
Nr Moreton in Marsh
Gloucestershire
GL56 9BB   Tel: 01386 701545

The tearooms are located in an early eighteenth century Coach House and Stables diagonally across the square from the Post Office. Locally is Farm Park and lovely walks in this area of beautiful countryside.

Cream Teas comprise scone, butter, jam and cream with a pot of tea for a very reasonable £1.70. Farmhouse Ice Cream is a speciality, and light lunches, such as a home made soup of the day, and home made cakes are offered on the menu. Sunday lunches are also a feature here.

Hours of business:
Daily - 10.30am to 5pm.

——— oOo ———

Tea, A Poem

Tea! How I tremble at thy fatal stream?
As Lethe, dreadful to the Love of Fame.
What devastations on thy banks are seen
What shades of mighty Names which once have been
A hecatomb of Characters supplies
Thy painted Altar's daily sacrifice.

(Aaron Ward)

The Quays Tea Room & Riverside Garden
45 Cartway
Bridgnorth   Parking   within 100m
Shropshire
WV16 4BG   Tel: 01746 737231

Situated on the scenic banks of the River Severn by the old bridge, the Quays Tea Room is not far from the cliff railway and Bishop Percy's house. Also in the area are the Severn Valley Railway and the Castle ruins and walk. The proprietor, Sue McCorquodale, is happy to provide local maps and information for her guests.

The house, a listed building, was built about 1650 and has a large inglenook fireplace and a host of old ships' timber as beams and purlins.

Scones are baked daily; home made cakes and soup are also on the menu here. There is no set afternoon tea, but regularly changing 'specials' assist guests in their choice.   The home made cakes are all listed on the blackboard, and a delicious range of sandwiches are made to order. Speciality teas are available, as well as filter coffee and a range of cold beverages.

Smoking is not permitted in the Tea Room, but guests may smoke on the patio when it is open.

Hours of business:
Tuesdays to Fridays - 10am to 5pm
Saturdays - 10am to 5.30pm
Sundays - 11am to 5.30pm
Closed on Mondays.

Northgate Pantry
Northgate Arcade
High Town   Parking - within 50m
Bridgnorth
Shropshire
WV16 4ER   Tel: 01746 767373

Located on the first floor, next to the Northgate Arch, the Pantry is near enough for visitors to take advantage of local places of interest such as the Severn Valley Railway, fishing on the River Severn, and sights within the market town itself.

All food is home cooked and proprietor Lisa Edwards offers a good range of naughty sweets and old fashioned puds, including bread pudding, Barm Bratch and lots more! The main teas available at this warm and welcoming establishment are Assam, Darjeeling and Earl Grey.

Hours of business:
Mondays to Saturdays - 10am to 5pm.
Sundays - 11am to 5pm.

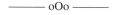

Lobster Mayonnaise Sandwich

Shred the lobster meat. Pour the mayonnaise over, add the yolks of three eggs and stir. Add half a teaspoon of salt, a little cayenne and white pepper, a pinch of nutmeg, half a mustard spoon, half of teaspoon of lemon juice, three drops of tarragon vinegar and a teaspoon of anchovy sauce.

(Five O'Clock Tea, 1886)

Flappers
The Square   Disabled Access
1 Church Road   Parking - within 50m
Codsall
Wolverhampton
WV8 1EA   Tel: 01902 845562

Flappers tea room is combined with a lovely card and gift shop situated in a paved area opposite 'The Crown', and it is only a short distance from the M54 and M6.

Locally there are individual shops and services, woods to explore, gentle walks nearby, and places to visit include Weston Park and RAF Cosford.

The menu includes a range of beverages, cold bites, light bites, hot bites, mixed bites, home made desserts and cakes and a wonderful assortment of flavours of Top House Farm Dairy Ice Cream, such as Turkish Delight, Pistachio, Butterscotch and many more. Don't miss the brown oat fruit crumble or the scrumptious home made fruit loaf! Home made cakes and scones can be ordered so that you can take an extra treat away with you.

Hours of business:
Mondays to Saturdays 8.30am to 6pm.

——— oOo ———

Tea does our fancy aid,
Repress those vapours which the head invade
and keeps the palace of the soul serene
Fit on her birthday to salute the Queen.

(Edmund Waller)

Bunty's
4-6 Hay Lane   Disabled Access
Coventry   Parking - within 100m
West Midlands
CV1 5BF   Tel: 01203 223758

Situated near Coventry's famous Cathedral and not far from the attractions of the British Transport Museum and the Lady Godiva Statue, Bunty's tea rooms can be found as an ideal respite for afternoon tea.

The menu offers teas, coffees, cakes and a variety of light lunches.

Hours of business:
Open from Whitsun to November -
Mondays to Saturdays 9.30am to 6pm
Sundays 10am to 5pm

——— oOo ———

This is the most magnificent movement of all! There is a dignity, a majesty, a sublimity, in this last effort of the patriots that I greatly admire.

The people should never rise without doing something to be remembered - something notable and striking. This destruction of the tea is so bold, so daring, so firm, intrepid and inflexible, and it must have so important consequences, and so lasting, that I cannot consider it as an epocha in history!

(John Adams' Diary on the day of the Boston Tea Party,
17 December, 1773)

Mr Pickwick's Tea Room

Brook Farm   Disabled Access
Stoneleigh Road   Parking - on premises
Coventry
West Midlands
CV4 7AB   Tel: 01203 693547

Located on the road to Warwick University and handy for Christmas tree sales in winter and fruit picking in summer, Mr Pickwick's Tea Room is housed in a converted tractor shed on a fruit picking farm, set beside a brook with a waterfall.

Inside, olde worlde décor with wooden beams, a tiled floor, pine furniture and hops brings back memories of a bygone age. Pictures from Dickens' Pickwick Papers adorn the walls. A riverside patio is available for summer barbeques and sunny afternoon teas.

Afternoon Tea comprises a scone with jam and cream, a slice of fruit cake and tea for one. In season strawberries and cream accompany the scone. There are various combinations, with home made cakes and scones tempting the customer. Specialities include apple cakes and pies, carrot cakes and bread and butter pudding. Mr Pickwick's Tea is a special blend from Ashby's, who also supply the coffee blends.

Hours of business:
Open seven days a week:
Summer: Sundays 10am to 5.30pm
                   Mondays to Wednesdays 10am to 4.30pm
                   Thursdays to Fridays 10am to 5pm
                   Saturdays 9.30am to 6pm
Winter: closing time is half an hour earlier than in summer .

Crumb's Tea Rooms
3 Southam Road
Dunchurch   Parking - within 50m
Nr Rugby
Warwickshire
CV22 6NL   Tel: 01788 522489

Crumb's Tea Rooms overlook the hustle and bustle of the ancient village with its thatched cottages, stocks on the green, and Guy Fawkes house. The village is perhaps most famed for its role in the Gunpowder Plot of 1605. Crumb's Tea Rooms are located just off the A45 at Dunchurch.

Tastefully furnished and prettily decorated, it is a perfect retreat for light refreshment. The friendly atmosphere and waitress service give a traditional feel along with the china crockery and collection of teapots.

Cream Teas offer a choice of freshly made sandwich and a cream tea for two or large toasted teacakes. Cakes and scones are all home baked and the clotted cream is brought from Cornwall. Fresh coffee and tea wash it all down with a choice of PG Tips, Camomile, Darjeeling and Earl Grey.

Hours of business:
Daily - 10am to 4.30pm.
Closed on Mondays.

Eyam Tea Rooms
The Square
Eyam   Parking - within 50m
Hope Valley
Derbyshire
S32 5RB   Tel: 01433 631274

Eyam, known as "Queen of the Peak" and "Plague Village" has a rich history dating from at least 1500 BC. As well as Roman relics there is also a fine example of Celtic Cross and the stone houses of the village where the Plague destroyed nearly 80% of the population in the 1600s.

The Tea Rooms themselves are set in the village square, and exude olde worlde charm, and inside the deceptively spacious establishment, features include a grand piano and a selection of antiques for sale.

Eyam Cream Tea, the speciality, consists of two delicious scones, baked on view in their own ovens, with freshly whipped cream and strawberry jam, plus your choice of tea or bottomless cup of coffee.

Fruitcake Tea brings a generous portion of rich home made fruitcake, Wensleydale cheese, fresh seasonal fruits and whole Chinese walnuts, plus tea or coffee. And for a real change, why not try the Pot Pourri of Fruit; a banana sandwich, brandy snap and coconut dainties, served with seasonal fruits and nuts, plus your choice of any pot of tea or bottomless cup of coffee.

You will be spoilt for choice when faced with the Best Yorkshire Tea, one of the many speciality teas, fruit tea, herbal tea or one of the coffees on offer. A wonderful Afternoon Tea stop!

Hours of business:
Tuesdays to Sundays - 10.30am to 5.30pm
Closed on Mondays
Closed in December and January.

Hungry Horse Tea Room
Hungry Horse Craft Centre   Disabled Access
Weeford Road   Parking - on premises
Four Oaks
West Midlands
B75 6NA   Tel: 0121 323 3658

Close to Sutton Park and opposite the Moor Hall Hotel, the Hungry Horse
Tea Room is surrounded by beautiful countryside, looking out across the
fields of horses. The old farmhouse has a friendly atmosphere with an
outside patio which is used in summer. Children are welcome in the
healthy, non smoking environment, which is apparently frequented by a
ghost.

Set around the farmhouse are restored farm buildings which house a
wonderful array of craft shops, including dried flowers, lingerie, modern
art, aromatherapy, garden furniture, mediterranean house wares and pine
furniture to name a few.

As you enter the tea rooms, you are welcomed by Mavis and Sue, and the
staff continue this cheerful message as they serve you at your table. The
majority of the food is home made, and guests are at liberty to create their
own afternoon tea from the wonderful fare on the blackboard. The portions
are generous and the tastes superb! In particular, the Bakewell tart and the
carrot cake should not be missed! A full range of hot and cold drinks are
available to complement your food.

Hours of business:
Tuesdays to Sundays - 10am to 5pm
Closed Mondays except Bank Holidays.

The Antique Teashop

5a St Peters Street

Hereford

Herefordshire

HR1 2LA

Disabled Access

Parking - within 50m

Tel: 01432 342172

The building is early Georgian and is on the site of St Peter's Monastery, next to St Peter's Church, and is situated in the pedestrian area. There is plenty to see around this market town deep in the Wye Valley.

The tables with linen cloths and fresh flowers do not seem unusual in a tea room, but what is different is that the guests sit on and at antique furniture that is for sale. Tables and chairs are also available outside for those who wish to take their refreshment al fresco. Pictures on the walls and mirrors are also for sale, making this a highly individual place to stop for refreshment.

Traditional Cream Tea, at just £3.65, and served on bone china, is a home made scone with clotted cream, strawberry jam and a pot of tea. For a fuller meal, Traditional Afternoon Tea for £9.75, provides the above, and in addition, there is a selection of finger sandwiches and home made cakes or pastries. A refreshing, healthy option is available with the Cottage Cheese Fruit Platter.

Hours of business:

All year round - Mondays to Fridays 9.45am to 5.30pm (except in July and August when closing time is 6pm), Saturdays 9.45am to 6pm, Sundays and Bank Holidays 9.45am to 5.30pm.

The Old Bakehouse
6 Tower Street
Ludlow
Shropshire
SY8 1Rl

Disabled Access
Parking - within 50m

Tel: 01584 872645

Originally a 17th century bakehouse, the tea rooms are situated in a pedestrianised street near to the town centre. Interesting local attractions include the Castle, Church, Whitcliff Common and Riverside Walks.

The homely Old Bakehouse offers different types of home made scones and speciality teas and coffees. There is a fuller menu and a supper menu on Saturday evenings.

Hours of business:
Mondays to Fridays 9am to 5pm
Saturdays 9am to 9pm
Sundays 10am to 6pm
Closed on Christmas Day.

——— oOo ———

It frequently breakfasts at five-o'clock tea,
and dines on the following day.

(Lewis Carroll)

Roseannes Tea Rooms

27 Market Street   Disabled Access
Lutterworth   Parking - on premises
Leicestershire
LE17 4QE   Tel: 01455 552212

Found opposite the Co-op, Roseannes Tea Rooms are close to the church made famous by John Wycliffe. On Thursdays there is a market in Lutterworth with fresh fruit and vegetables and many interesting stalls. Living up to the name, roses feature in the décor, with rose china and border. There is also an unusual collection of teapots which add to the character of this cosy tea room.

There is no set menu, which allows greater freedom of choice for the guest. Sandwiches and rolls are freshly prepared to order, with the option of low fat or fat free spreads. A range of light lunches are available, plus a selection of cakes and pastries listed on the daily specials board. Speciality teas, coffees and cold drinks are also on the menu.

Hours of business:
Mondays to Saturdays - 9am to 5.30pm
Open Sundays by request.

——— oOo ———

Samson

Mix one bottle of Claret, one of champagne, two of soda water and a wine glass of sherry. Add 6 strawberries and 4 tablespoons of sifted sugar.
Always add the sugar slowly, just before serving.

(Five O'Clock Tea, 1886)

Lady Foley's Tea Room
Great Malvern Station   Disabled Access
Imperial Road   Parking - on premises
Malvern
Worcestershire
WR14 3AT   Tel: 01684 893033

Set on the platform of a very attractive Victorian railway station which has won awards and been used for television plays, Lady Foley's Tea Room offers tables on the platform for train lovers to watch the trains, whilst inside the décor is in keeping with the building. The picturesque Malvern Hills are a local attraction.

Tea supplies the guest with a sandwich, a home baked scone with jam and cream and a pot of tea. Cakes, scones and lunches are all home baked and include goodies like cherry and pineapple cake, date, apple and walnut and lemon meringue pie. Teas include Assam, Darjeeling, Earl Grey, herb teas and Lady Foley's own blend.

Hours of business:
Mondays to Saturdays - 9am - 6pm
Sundays - 3pm to 6pm.

——— oOo ———

(Tar water) is of a nature so mild and benign
and proportioned to the human constitution as
to warm without heating, to cheer but not inebriate.

(Bishop George Berkeley, 1744)

Mamble Tea Room
Mamble Craft Centre   Disabled Access
Church Lane   Parking - on premises
Mamble
Nr Bewdley
Worcestershire
DY14 9JY   Tel: 01299 832834

The Tea Room is set in 17th century barns with wonderful exposed timbers, next to the 13th century village church. It is attached to Mamble Craft Centre which houses a craft gallery, exhibition room, gift shop, workshops, and where demonstrations and courses are held. All areas have disabled access except for the craft gallery. There is free admission to the Craft Centre and parking is also free.

There are stunning views across rolling fields to the Shropshire Clee Hills and beyond to the Black Mountains of Wales. You will find Mamble, a beautiful Worcestershire village, off the A456 halfway between Bewdley and Tenbury Wells.

Large scones are served with the cream teas, and there are lots of different 'naughty' cakes to tempt you! A superb range of delicious and unusual fillings for baked potatoes, sandwiches and toasted sandwiches are on the menu, plus a variety of specials that change frequently.

A satisfying range of hot and cold beverages are on offer to quench your thirst, including Earl Grey tea and decaffeinated coffee.

Hours of business:
Open all year round
Tuesdays to Saturdays - 10.30am to 5pm
Sundays and Bank Holidays - 11.30am to 5.30pm
Closed on Mondays.

Melbourne Hall Tea Rooms

Blackwell Lane   Disabled Access
Melbourne   Parking - within 100m
Derby
Derbyshire
DE73 1EN   Tel: 01332 864224

Located in the grounds of Melbourne Hall, near to St Michael's Parish Church, the tea rooms are close to the craft centre and the lake. Built around 1710, the premises were originally the wash house/bake house of the Hall. The original bakers oven is still in position. The tea rooms have their own courtyard, which today is used for patrons in fine weather.

A set tea is available for parties at £4.25 a head, comprising assorted sandwiches, scones, jam, a home made cake and limitless tea. Alternatively, a simpler tea of two scones with jam, cream and a pot of tea is served.

Cakes and scones are home made and the teas available include Ceylon and Earl Grey. In addition to afternoon teas, morning coffee, and light lunches are also served.

Hours of business:
Tuesdays to Sundays - 11am to 5pm
Closed on Mondays.
Restricted opening times in January and February - telephone to check.

Ollerton Watermill Teashop
Market Place
Ollerton   Parking - on premises
Newark
Nottinghamshire
NG22 9AA   Tel: 01623 822469

Situated opposite the War Memorial ground and near to Rufford Country Park and Sherwood Forest, the home of Robin Hood, the teashop is an 18th century watermill which has been restored. The entrance is at the back of the waterwheel, over the mill race, with a glass viewing panel. Overlooking the river Mawn with magnificent views upstream; often with swans and ducks paddling gracefully by, this venue is a delightful place to relax.

The décor is pine with white walls, and spotlessly clean tables are set with china and fresh greenery.

All the baking is done on the premises using flour sold in the mill. Portions are generous and the outstanding quality has won the Ollerton Mill Teashop "Best Afternoon Tea" award twice. Ollerton Mill Cream Tea provides a pot of tea and a choice of plain or fruit scones with fresh cream and jam, The Bakewell Tart or Carrot cake make a tempting alternative. In addition to the house blend, the teas are Darjeeling, Earl Grey, Assam, Lady Grey, Lapsang Souchong, Jasmine and Rose Pouchong.

Hours of business:
March to November - Tuesdays to Sundays 10.30am to 5pm.
Open Bank Holiday Mondays.
Closed December to February.
Evening group visits, including a guided tour of the Mill and refreshment afterward in the teashop, can be arranged.

Chancellors Tea Rooms
and Licensed Restaurant
Victoria Street   Disabled Access
Painswick   Parking - within 100m
Gloucestershire
CL6 6QA   Tel: 01452 812451

Set in the centre of the village near the stocks and the church, the Chancellors Tea Rooms are within easy reach of Painswick House and gardens. The Grade II listed building in Cotswold stone with oak beams is an ideal setting for a traditional English Tea.

Cream Tea comprises two scones, jam, cream and a pot of tea, and the Chancellor's Special Afternoon Tea offers egg mayonnaise and cress sandwich, home made fruit scone with butter and jam, and a pot of tea. Scones and cakes are home made and teacakes can be served with a special cinnamon butter, which is absolutely delicious!

Among a good selection of teas are the old favourites Assam, Ceylon, China, Darjeeling and Earl Grey. Also available at Chancellors are Morning Coffee, light lunches, sandwiches and a selection of take away foods.

Hours of business:
Weekdays and Saturdays - 10.30am to 5pm (closed on Wednesdays)
Sundays - 12 to 5pm.

Brook Farm Tea Rooms

Brook Farm   Disabled Access
Brook End   Parking - on premises
Repton
Derbyshire
DE65 6FW   Tel: 01283 702215

Brook Farm Tea Rooms are housed in a converted sandstone barn in a brookside location, 150 yards from the centre of the historic village of Repton. They are within easy reach of Calke Abbey and Foremarke Reservoir. The large, private lawned garden offers outside seating in summer.

Farmhouse Tea includes a round of freshly cut sandwiches, home made scone with butter and jam, and a pot of tea for £3.20. Brook Farm Tea includes two home made scones, jam and cream and a pot of tea for just £2.95. Cakes and scones are home made and teas include Assam, Darjeeling and Earl Grey, plus a selection of fruit teas. The locally made Real Farmhouse Dairy Ice Cream boasts many unusual flavours. A variety of home cooked lunches and sweets are available daily.

Giving a relaxed, rural experience and friendly waitress service, it is easy to see why this venue is Egon Ronay recommended. It is also a founder member of the Tea Council and Guild of Tea Shops.

Hours of business:
Wednesdays to Mondays - 10am to 4.30pm (last orders)
Closed on Tuesdays
Closed Christmas and January.

Kent House Country Kitchen

Ridgeway Craft Centre   Disabled Access
Ridgeway Village   Parking - on premises
Derbyshire
S12 3XR   Tel: 0114 247 3739

Opposite "The Swan" Inn, the Kent House Country Kitchen is minutes away from various walks along the Moss Valley. While the tea room is situated within the old farmhouse, the craft centre is on the premises of the old Kent House Farm.

The building is three hundred years old, and features a farmhouse kitchen with the original Yorkshire range and oak beams.

The delicious cakes and scones are home made, and the teas available include China and Earl Grey. Also available are hot and cold meals, sandwiches and snacks.

Hours of business:
Open Tuesdays through to Sundays.
Closed Mondays except Bank Holidays.

——— oOo ———

Don't pour out tea before putting sugar in the cup,
or someone will be drowned.

(American Negro Proverb)

The Antique Teashop
40 High Street
Ross on Wye   Parking - within 50m
Herefordshire
HR9 5SW   Tel: 01989 566123

The Antique Teashop is found to the side of the Market Hall in the borders market town of Ross on Wye, with its attractions of the Prospect Walk, St Mary's Church and the Button Museum.

In common with its sister establishment in Hereford, guests sit on antique chairs and at tables that are for sale. Linen table cloths, fresh flowers and bone china complete the refined atmosphere.

Traditional Afternoon Tea provides a selection of finger sandwiches, a home made scone with clotted cream and strawberry jam, together with home made cakes and pastries, together with a pot of tea or coffee. The Cottage Cheese Fruit Platter is a healthy option.

The Antique Shop has a sister establishment in Hereford that is well worth visiting as you pass through.

Hours of business:
All year round -
Mondays to Fridays 9.45am to 5.30pm
(except in July and August when closing time is 6pm)
Saturdays 9.45am to 6pm
Sundays and Bank Holidays 9.45am to 5.30pm.

Meg Rivers Tea Room

23A High Street   Disabled Access
Shipston-on-Stour   Parking - within 50m
Warwickshire
CV36 4AJ   Tel: 01608 662217

Situated on the High Street, behind Lloyds Bank and at the bottom of Sheep Street, Meg Rivers Tea Room combines elegance and a quiet relaxed atmosphere where visitors can enjoy the view up Sheep Street with its charming 16th and 17th century buildings. Pretty blue and white china and fresh flowers complete the traditional English Tea Room ambience. Upton House, Hidcote Manor, Whichford Pottery and Crossin Cottage Gallery are all local attractions.

Cream Tea can be served at any time of the day, comprising two plain scones with strawberry jam, fresh thick cream and a pot of tea or coffee. All the cakes, biscuits, scones and shortbreads are hand baked at the Meg Rivers Bakery in Tysoe using only the finest ingredients. A range of teas are offered including Traditional English Tea, Earl Grey, Darjeeling, Assam and Camomile, and filter and decaffeinated coffees. The menu also provides for delicious soup and savouries.

A speciality here is the Picnic Hamper Basket Service, where a quality hamper packed full of delicious lunch and afternoon treats is prepared to order, and also Music on a Sunday afternoon, where a musician will add to the traditional atmosphere between 3 and 5pm whilst guests enjoy their afternoon tea.

Hours of business:
Mondays to Saturdays 10am to 5pm
Sundays and Bank Holidays 12.30pm to 5pm.

Meg Rivers Tea Room, Shipston on Stour

Bensons of Stratford upon Avon
4 Bards Walk   Disabled Access
Stratford upon Avon   Parking - within 100m
Warwickshire
CV37 6EY   Tel: 01789 261116

In the centre of Stratford upon Avon, just two minutes from Shakespeare's birthplace and not far from Mary Arden's House and Ann Hathaways cottage, Bensons epitomises the atmosphere and tradition of English culture, with friendly staff dressed in pinstripe uniforms. Established for over five years, Bensons has built a reputation for fine food and products with exceptional service.

Fine bone china and silver tableware, fresh flowers, menus reproduced onto a 1936 copy of the Daily Telegraph enhance this gracious establishment.

Smoked salmon sandwiches with freshly squeezed lemon and ground pepper, a freshly baked scone with cream and jam, or a selection from the internationally renowned French patisserie Maison Blanc; the menu is extensive and tempting!

Afternoon Tea at Bensons is a real event! From freshly baked scones or traditional toasted teacakes to Full Traditional English Afternoon Tea, the real treat has to be Champagne Tea for which booking is essential.

To complement this delicious range of food, the very extensive selection of teas, tisanes, coffees and cold beverages is second to none!

Hours of business:
Mondays to Saturdays - 9am to 5.15pm
Sundays - 11am to 4.30pm.
Closed on Sundays January to March.

The Roaches Tea Rooms

Paddock Farm   Disabled Access
Upper Hulme   Parking - on premises
Nr Leek
Staffordshire
ST13 8TY   Tel: 01538 300345

You will find The Roaches Tea Rooms three miles out of Leek, on the A53 - look for the white teapot sign at Upper Hulme village. Situated by the Roaches, overlooking Tittesworth Reservoir, the area is popular with walkers and climbers. It is also conveniently situated for Alton Towers, and for the factory shops and antique shops at Leek.

Views from the tea room are magnificent, and inside, the oak beams and inglenook fireplace with a wood burning stove, give a cosy atmosphere. A grandfather clock, Welsh dresser, oak corner cupboard and settle add to the homely ambience. The conservatory makes it a pleasant setting for tea, or in warmer weather, you may choose a table outside on the patio, by the herb garden. Disabled access to the tea rooms and the patio is possible via the ramps, but there are presently no toilet facilities for the disabled.

With home made cakes, desserts and soup, local honey and free range eggs, there is a real local taste to the fare here. Delicious fruit loaf, fruit pie and crumble, and pavlova with fresh cream and fruit topping are among the choices, and the range of teas include some very refreshing herb teas.

Hours of business:
Summer time -   open every day from 9am to 7pm.
Winter time -   Mondays - closed
                   Tuesdays until Fridays - 9am to 4pm
                   Saturdays and Sundays - 9am to 6pm.
Closed from Christmas Eve to Boxing Day inclusive.

Wales

The Old Tea Rooms

Church Street   Disabled Access
Barmouth   Parking - within 50m
Gwynedd
Wales
LL42 1EG   Tel: 01341 280194

The Old Tea Rooms are found in beautifully converted cottages which date back to 1720. Located in the main street near to the harbour and old St David's Church, they are also in the vicinity of two miles of clean sandy beaches, which hold the Blue Flag Award. There is boating and fishing, and stunning views of the estuary where mountains meet the sea.

With an inglenook fireplace and exposed beams from old ships masts and spars, the tea rooms are light, airy and clean. The tables are set with crocheted tea cloths on top of the table cloths and beautiful fresh flowers. There is a no smoking policy throughout. The welcome from June Edwards, the proprietor, is warm and genuine, and all the food is freshly prepared for the guests.

Well dressed, friendly and polite staff serve Welsh Afternoon and Cream Teas which offer Welsh Cakes, Bara Brith, Welsh Tea Bread and Welsh scones. There is a superb variety of cakes and gateaux, and a speciality is the new range of Gourmet sandwiches made with a range of breads such as fresh rye bread or walnut bread.

Hours of business:
Summer season (1st April to 30th September):
Open every day except Wednesdays - 10.30am to 5pm
Winter season (1st October to 31st March):
Open Thursdays to Sundays 10.30am to 5pm
Closed for the last two weeks of January.

The Copper Kettle
103 The Struet   Disabled Access
Brecon   Parking - within 50m
Powys
LD3 7LT   Tel: 01874 611349

Situated between Woolworth and Kwik Save, this Grade II listed olde worlde tea and coffee shop is ideally situated for weary walkers and visitors to the Brecon Beacons. Inside it has oak beams, and displays prints by local and internationally known artists in the coffee lounge.

The owner, Mrs Helga Debroy Summers, is a former hotelier, who was born in Switzerland, where she did her training. English, German and Welsh are spoken at The Copper Kettle, award winning Best Coffee Shop in Wales.

Welsh Cream Teas are served with a selection of herbal teas available, together with China, Darjeeling and Earl Grey, and various coffees. There are speciality Welsh cakes and a Swiss patisserie to select from, as well as a full menu of light lunches and cooked meals.

The warm welcome here is captured by the farewell greeting on the menu; "Thank you for calling, we shall keep the kettle boiling until next time...."!

Hours of business:
Open all year -
Mondays to Saturdays 8am to 5.30pm
Sundays 10am to 5.30pm.

Cenarth Tearooms & Gift Shop

Cenarth

Nr Newcastle Emlyn

Carmarthenshire

SA38 9JL

Parking - within 50m

Tel: 01239 711213

Situated next to the National Coracle Centre with its 17th century water mill, Cenarth Tearooms are about fifty metres from the famous salmon leap waterfalls, the home of the coracle fishermen, and which are renowned worldwide for their outstanding beauty.

Cenarth itself is a conservation village with many fine walks featuring the local nature and history. The Tearooms are on two levels, with a model village and historic pictures in the basement. Disabled access to the tearooms is restricted by two steps but during summer months, there is easy access to the garden. Tables and chairs are in matching dark wood and there are flowers on all the tables, with waiting service inside and outside in the garden.

Welsh Tea comprises a pot of tea, a scone with butter, jam and fresh cream from a local farm, and bara brith with butter. Cream Tea serves a pot of tea, a scone with butter, jam and fresh cream. Also on the menu is locally made ice cream, and a selection of salads, sandwiches and cakes. Prices are very reasonable and cakes are all home baked. Teas include Assam, Darjeeling, Earl Grey and Lemon.

Before you leave, take a look at the extensive range of slateware, terracotta and other Welsh crafts for sale in the gift shop.

Hours of business.

Mid-March to end of October - daily 10am to 6pm.

Closed November to mid March.

St Mary's Tearooms
5 St Mary's Street   Disabled Access
Chepstow   Parking - within 50m
Monmouthshire
NP6 5EU   Tel: 01291 621711

Proprietors Michael and Linda Johns aim to give everyone personal service in the attractively decorated tea room. Otherwise, there is waitress service for visitors who can sit outside at the tables set in the cobbled street, or in the enclosed courtyard to the rear in warm weather, and separate tea rooms are available for smokers and non smokers.

The tearooms are located just off the High Street, opposite the church. Local attractions in this particularly scenic area are Chepstow Castle, the Wye Valley, Tintern Abbey and the Forest of Dean.

Cream Tea comprises two scones with jam, butter, clotted cream and a pot of tea, for £2.80. Specialities include the locally made farm ice creams from the Wye Valley, as well as a very wide range of teas and coffees from around the world, including real cappucino and espresso coffees.

Local dishes are a speciality, with Welsh Rarebit cooked to Michael and Linda's own recipe, home made pies and cakes and home made soups.

Hours of business:
All year round - Mondays to Saturdays - 9am to 5pm
Closed on Sundays
Early closing during winter months.

The Old Station Coffee Shop

Dinas Mawddwy

Machynlleth

Powys

SY20 9LS

Disabled Access

Parking - on premises

Tel: 01650 531338

The Old Station Coffee Shop is set amongst outstanding mountain scenery, and is on the right of the entrance to Meirion Mill. It was originally the waiting room and booking hall of the Mawddwy Railway Station, which took passengers and slate seven miles down the Dyfi Valley. Located on the A470 one mile north of the junction with A458 at Mallwyd roundabout, on the left hand side of the road.

A book with the full history of the station and area is on sale in the shop for just £1.50, along with other items such as preserves and chocolates. The coffee shop still retains the original 1860 fireplaces and there is seating outside on fine days.

There is no set menu for afternoon tea, except for parties, who, for only £3.80 per person, are provided with sandwiches, Welsh cake, Bara Brith, cream cake and endless tea! Individual customers may select any of these items from the menu, and also may choose from two home made soups, savoury flan, cakes, biscuits and scones. If you time your visit right, mouthwatering fresh scones hot from the oven are served at 10.30am!

Hours of business:
Easter to end of October - daily 9.30am to 5pm
Reduced hours in winter - telephone to check.

"Planters"
Tal Goed Nurseries
Glan Conwy
Conwy

Disabled Access
Parking - on premises

Tel: 01492 573073

Planters is positioned in Conwy Valley with wonderful views of the surrounding countryside. Easily accessed from the A55 to Conwy Valley, on leaving Glan Conwy Village, take the 2nd turning on the left after Water Mill.

This very unusual setting for tea is inside a large greenhouse, giving views from all aspects, with a light and sunny atmosphere. The tea room is adjacent to nurseries and a fruit farm, so it is equally attractive to the tea lover, the fruit picker or the ardent gardener!

The friendly, helpful staff serve guests from a well designed menu, that offers Afternoon Teas, home made soups, pies and daily specials. The delicious Planters Afternoon Tea comprises a pot of tea, your choice of tuna, cheese, egg or cucumber sandwich, and a scone with jam and cream.

Speciality teas are available, including Assam, Earl Grey, Darjeeling, and a range of Fruit teas. Other beverages includes Bewleys coffee and a selection of soft drinks.

Hours of business:
Open seven days a week - 9.30am to 5pm
Closed from 24th December until the first weekend after New Year.
Open weekends only during January.

**The Drovers Rest Restaurant
and Tea Rooms**

The Square   Disabled Access
Llanwrtyd Wells   Parking - within 50m
Powys
LD5 4RE   Tel: 01591 610264

Llanwrtyd Wells, an old spa town on the banks of the River Irfon, almost mid-way between Builth Wells and Llandovery on the A483, is flanked by the Cambrian Mountains on one side, and the Mynydd Eppynt on the other; providing a variety of magnificent unspoilt scenery. The attractive 18th century restaurant and tea rooms, tastefully restored, is situated in the centre of this Mid-Wales town.

Home made and traditional food is prepared on the premises, utilising fresh, local produce whenever possible. The Special Welsh Tea consists of wholemeal bread and butter, Caerphilly cheese, tomato and melon and bara brith as well as Welsh cakes, home made scones with cream and jam, and a pot of tea with milk, lemon or honey. Scrumptious! Toasted teacakes are somewhat larger than the average teacake, and the special choice of cakes made by patissiere, Paulette Reed, includes the mouthwatering lemon crunch! Ice creams and sorbets are made on the premises too.

The tea room and restaurant with its superb menu has gained its owner, Peter James, a coveted 'Taste of Wales' award and a place in Egon Ronay's 'Good Food Guide' - quite rightly so!

Hours of business:
Daily from 9.30am to 5pm
Fridays, Saturdays and Sundays - from 7.30pm for dinner.
Closed Christmas Day and New Year's Eve.

The Tearoom
Manorbier Garden Centre   Disabled Access
Station Road   Parking - on premises
Manorbier
Nr Tenby
Pembrokeshire
SA70 7SN   Tel: 01834 871678

Near to Manorbier Castle, beach and historic village, The Tearoom is off the B41 just one mile outside the village between Lydstep and Jameston, and situated between the school and the station.

With a cosy, friendly atmosphere it is well patronised by local Pembrokeshire people - they seem to know a good thing when they see it! There is a pretty tea garden surrounded by colourful plants and mature trees.

The speciality products here vary according to season, as the proprietors, Liz and Roger Thompson, aim to use mainly locally grown produce; fruit, vegetables, cheeses, butter and clotted cream. Most of the items on the very reasonably priced menu are home made on the premises, including the meringues, gateaux, Welsh cakes and vegetarian dishes. Don't miss the delicious millionaires shortbread or butterfly cakes!

Hours of business:
Open seven days a week 10am to 5pm
Closed Christmas Day and Boxing Day.

The Bank Cottage Tea Rooms

The Bank   Disabled Access
Newtown   Parking - within 50m
Powys
SY16 2AB   Tel: 01686 625771

Newtown is situated in the middle of Wales with the River Severn running through the town. The Bank Cottage Tea Rooms are in a beautiful oak framed 16th century listed building, which has been restored to its original glory, featuring a log fire in winter and a wealth of wooden beams inside and out. Antique tables and chairs, period cutlery and Willow pattern tableware add to the traditional atmosphere.

The proprietor, Jane Shrimpton, offers a varied menu, which contains a good selection of vegetarian and vegan specials, alongside the traditional tea room fare, and Jane welcomes you for morning coffee, luncheon or afternoon tea.

Cream Tea consists of two home made scones, jam and cream with a pot of tea. Welsh Tea constitutes two slices of wholemeal bread, two jams, a choice of cake and a pot of tea. Cakes, scones and jams are all home made, and fruit for the pies and jams is home grown.

Along with a lovely variety of fruit and herbal teas, coffees and cold drinks, Darjeeling and Earl Grey feature as the favourite teas.

Hours of business:
Open Mondays to Saturdays - 9am to 5pm.
Closed Sundays.
Open Bank Holidays.

The Millhouse Tea Room & Restaurant
The Mill House
Sarn Meillteyrn   Parking - on premises
Pwllheli
Gwynedd
LL53 8HF   Tel: 01758 730288

The Millhouse Tea Room is situated in the heart of the beautiful Lleyn Peninsula on the B4415, in the market village of Sarn Meillteyrn. In the village, you will find a potter, and also a furniture maker producing a range of woodcrafts.

The menu offers Cream Teas with a selection of home made scones and cakes, including the famous Welsh Bara Brith. A range of speciality teas and fruit cordials is always available. Morning coffee, snacks, lunches, teas and hot meals are served all day, and there is an extensive evening menu available. Reservations are taken for traditional Sunday lunch. Although the premises is not licensed, guests are welcome to bring their own wine to enjoy with their meal.

Also on sale is a range of novelty tea pots, mugs and jugs to remind you of your delicious afternoon tea!

Hours of business:
Every day - 10.45 am to 5pm
Closed from October to Easter.
Evening meals available - Wednesdays to Sundays 6-8.30pm (low season) and every day 6-8.30pm (high season).

Carole's Cake Shop and Tearooms

Old Swan   Disabled Access
West Street   Parking - within 50m
Rhayader
Powys
LD6 5AB   Tel: 01597 811060

Rhayader is a small market town to the east of the Cambrian mountains, the home of the Red Kite. Within easy reach of the Elan Valley Reservoirs, Gigrin Farm where you can see the Red Kites feeding, and the Welsh Royal Crystal Factory, Carole's Cake Shop and Tearooms is set on the crossroads in the town centre.

The Old Swan is one of the oldest buildings in Rhayader, dating from 1638, and has many original features, including a rare Welsh post and panel partition in the tearoom. Customers are requested not to smoke whilst visiting the tearoom.

Welsh Tea comprises a pot of tea, bread and butter, honey, home made jam, two Welsh cakes and Bara Brith, and is reasonably priced at £2.85. Cream Tea at £2.45 brings a pot of tea and two scones with jam and cream, and there are many other home made products on the menu to tempt the visitor; carrot cake, bara brith, Welsh cakes to name but a few. A range of Welsh hand made chocolates and Welsh preserves are on sale to remind you of your visit.

Hours of business:
Summer season -
Mondays to Saturdays - 9am to 5.30pm
Sundays - 10.30am to 6pm
Winter season -
Mondays to Saturdays - 9am to 5pm (except Thursday afternoons)
Sundays - 11am to 5pm

Bramleys Tearoom

Plough Penny Nursery
St Florence
Nr Tenby
Pembrokeshire
SA70 8LP

Disabled Access
Parking - on premises

Tel: 01834 871778

Bramleys Tearoom is situated in a rural nursery just outside the beautiful village of St Florence in the heart of South Pembrokeshire, about four miles from Tenby. Locally, you will find The Cheese Factory, Heatherton, Manor Park and the Dinosaur Park.

The tearoom run by Liz Hainsworth is set in a new Scandinavian style log cabin with a delightful ambience, where quality, customer care and friendliness are by-words. Guests can sit outside in the small garden or on the verandah in warm weather. The establishment is non smoking throughout.

For £2.25, the delicious cream tea consists of home made scones, jam and local clotted cream with a pot of tea. Many other choices are available and everything on the menu is home made using local products and ingredients.

Liz Hainsworth particularly recommends her specialities of Sewin fishcakes, chicken, leek and mushroom pie, Glamorgan sausages, and the blackberry and apple pie.

Bramleys has won a "Red Book" award for the best tearoom in Wales, and it is certainly well worth a visit.

Hours of business:
From 1st March to 31st October -
Open seven days a week - 10am to 5pm
For the rest of the year -
Open Thursdays to Sundays - 10am to 5pm

Celtic Fare Tea Rooms

Vernon House   Disabled Access
St Julians Street   Parking - within 100m
Tenby
Pembrokeshire
SA70 7AS   Tel: 01834 845258

Located just off Tudor Square on the way to the harbour and overlooking Caldey Island, the family run Celtic Fare Tea Rooms are part of the seaside town with its historic walls, castle and three beautiful beaches.

The old fashioned interior is charming with its wooden floors and authentic gas lamps in season which complement the fire burning in the Victorian hearth.

The clothed tables, matching crockery and tea served in china teapots by waitresses attired in turn of the century costume, create the impression of a more gracious age, as do the splendid selection of home baked cakes, puddings and pastries.

Cream Teas come with locally produced, thick, Caldey Island Clotted Cream, and the variety of teas include speciality teas from Twinings.

Hours of business:
Open all year round - 10am to 6pm.
Out of season - closed on Mondays and closing time on weekdays is 4-5pm.

Bronant Tea Rooms & Bistro

Bronant   Disabled Access
Ty-Nant   Parking - on premises
Corwen
Denbighshire
LL21 0PR   Tel: 01490 460344

You will find Bronant Tea Rooms halfway between Llangollen and Betws-y-coed, on the A5 and signposted with brown tourist signs. The Tea Rooms are close to the spectacular Snowdonia National Park, Bala Lake and the Denbigh Moors. Local attractions include the River Ceirw Gorge and Waterfall.

A former sixteenth century coach house, the beamed ceiling gives an historic feel to the venue, which faces the River Ceirw. Seating is available on the patio, surrounded by tubs of flowers. The tableware used is hand made pottery, and there is a gift shop on site where you may purchase mementos of your visit.

Choose from home made wholemeal scones, bara brith, Welsh Cakes or Teacakes, or from the bistro, local trout baked to perfection with lemon and almonds. Home made Steak and Kidney or Chicken and Mushroom pies are amongst the other menu items. Set menus include Welsh Cream Tea for £2.20,   Welsh Tea for £2.45, or the more substantial Welsh Farmhouse Tea for £4.40. There is a good selection of teas, including Assam, Ceylon, China, Darjeeling and Earl Grey.

Hours of business:
Mondays to Wednesdays - 10am to 5pm
Thursdays - 10am to 3pm
Fridays - 10am to 6pm
Saturdays - 10am to 6pm
Sundays - 10am to 7pm
Bookings only after 6.30pm.

Cefn Coch
Llanegryn
Tywyn   Parking - on premises
Gwynedd
LL36 9SD   Tel: 01654 712193

Visitors to the nearby Tal-y-Llyn narrow gauge railway or Llanegryn church, known for its exquisite carved wood screen, will find Cefn Coch a truly delightful place to rest and refresh themselves.

The tea rooms inhabit an old coaching inn set amongst the magnificent Welsh coastal and mountain scenery on the southern edge of the Snowdonia National Park. You will find Cefn Coch immediately on the left after turning off the A493 towards the village of Llanegryn.

Inside, tea served on traditional Wedgwood china, can be taken in the dining room, with its oak beamed ceiling and slate floor, set off by attractive Laura Ashley décor. Alternatively, tables are set out in the garden for guests to enjoy the fresh air as they partake of the freshly prepared food.

There is no set tea menu, allowing guests to select their own ideal afternoon tea from a range of sandwiches, light snacks and home made cakes, soups, pâtés and jams. Tea is a choice of the house blend, Earl Grey or herbal tea.

This establishment also provides accommodation - telephone for details.

Hours of business:
Open daily 11am to 4pm except Wednesdays when it is closed.

Market Hall Tea & Coffee Rooms
College Green
Tywyn   Parking - within 100m
Gwynedd
LL36 9BY   Tel: 01654 710733

Set in the Market Hall, a one hundred year old building in Tywyn, near to the Tal-y-Llyn Railway and Cader Idris, Market Hall Tea and Coffee Rooms have separate rooms available for smokers and non smokers.

Cakes and scones are home baked and there is a choice of tea and coffee.

Hours of business:
Closed on Sundays.
Closed half day on Mondays and Wednesdays.

——— oOo ———

THE POETS AT TEA
(Wordsworth)

"Come, little cottage girl, you seem
To want my cup of tea;
And will you take a little cream?
Now tell the truth to me."
She had a rustic, woodland grin
Her cheek was soft as silk,
And she replied, "Sir, please put in
A little drop of milk".

Barry Pain
1864-1928

Eastern Counties

Margaret's Tea Rooms
Chestnut Farmhouse
The Street   Parking - on premises
Baconsthorpe
Nr Holt
Norfolk
NR25 6AB   Tel: 01263 577614

Margaret's is situated in the main street of the village of Baconsthorpe, which is only a short distance from the Norfolk coast. Also in the locality are Holt, Sheringham and Cromer.

The 17th century flint farmhouse is divided into two tea rooms, the Harebell Parlour and the Strawberry Parlour. Lace tablecloths and a wintertime log burner contribute to the homely atmosphere, as does the No Smoking policy. Proprietors Margaret and Roger Bacon are Heartbeat Award winners for their healthy menu options.

The scrumptious cakes, pastries, scones, bread and jam are baked by Margaret herself in the farmhouse kitchen. Cream Tea offers two scones with jam and fresh cream and tea. Muffin Tea comprises toasted muffin with butter and jam or honey, a portion of cake chosen from the Pembroke table and a pot of tea.

Morning coffee, light lunches and afternoon tea are all served from a selection that changes day to day. The selection may include delicious pies, flans, coffee and walnut cake, victoria sponge and bread pudding. A wonderful choice of twenty different teas include Assam, Ceylon, Darjeeling and Earl Grey, and there are also six coffees and a range of fruit juices and cordials to quench the thirst.

Hours of business:
Easter to November - Tuesdays to Sundays 10.30am to 5pm
Closed on Mondays except Bank Holidays
November to Easter - Saturdays and Sundays only 10am to 5pm.

The Crooked Cottage Tea Rooms
1 The Quay
Burnham on Crouch   Parking - within 50m
Essex
CM0 8AS   Tel: 01621 783868

Close to the yacht harbour and riverside walks, the tea rooms are housed in listed buildings, being three hundred and fifty year old fishermen's cottages on the quayside. Local attractions include the Railway Museum, Country Park, walks along the River Crouch and sailing.

Original timber beams and brick fireplaces give an olde worlde ambience inside, while in warm weather guests can sit in the Victorian rose garden, where there is a fish pond and an abundance of cats! There is waitress service and children are welcome.

Cream Tea serves a pot of tea or coffee, Tiptree jam, fresh cream and two home made scones for just £3.10. Cakes are also home baked and the establishment offers a choice of eighteen types of leaf tea, including favourites Assam, Ceylon, China, Darjeeling and Earl Grey.

Sunday lunch is a speciality here, so take a pleasant stroll along the River Crouch between your lunch and afternoon tea!

Hours of business:
Tuesdays to Sundays - 10am to 5.30pm
Closed Mondays - except for Bank Holidays.
Open at weekends only from November to end of February.

Aunties Tea Shop
1 St Mary's Passage
Cambridge
Cambridgeshire
CB2 3PQ   Tel: 01223 315641

Established in 1980, Aunties Tea Shop is opposite Great St Mary's Church
and adjacent to Kings Parade, which houses Kings College and the Senate
House, where ceremonies to award students their degrees are held. There
is much to see in this area; the colleges of Cambridge university,
Fitzwilliam Museum, the churches and the Cambridge city centre.

These traditional English tea rooms are situated in an historic building,
which is decorated in Victorian style, with lace tablecloths, waitresses
attired in uniforms, and tables available outside in the summer.

Proprietor Yvonne Prevett offers Aunties Special Cream Tea, a traditional
cream tea comprising an egg and cress sandwich, two of their famous
scones, jam and cream, and a pot of English breakfast tea, all for just
£3.95. There is also a superb range of open sandwiches on the menu,
featuring excellent combinations of ingredients.

Also available are the mouthwatering home made specialities, 'hot' banana
cake with butterscotch sauce and cream, and 'hot' gingerbread served with
maple syrup and cream, which are free from artificial flavourings and
preservatives. To wash it all down, the selection of teas includes Assam,
Ceylon, China, Darjeeling and Earl Grey.

Hours of business:
Mondays to Fridays 9.30am to 6pm
Saturdays 9.30am to 6.30pm
Sundays 12.00 to 5.30pm.

Marples Tea Rooms
6 Seaview Street   Disabled Access
Cleethorpes   Parking - within 50m
Lincolnshire
DN35 8EZ   Tel: 01472 697188

Situated in the old part of Cleethorpes, Seaview Street provides a good selection of gift, antique and interior design shops. Marples Tea Rooms is set at the sea front end of the street and is based on the famous Miss Marple theme.

Proprietors David and Sheila Allen pride their establishment on a high level of customer service and high quality products, served in a relaxing and old fashioned environment, where the waitresses wear traditional black dresses and evoke memories of days gone by.

Marples Full Afternoon Tea comprises freshly cut sandwiches, a scone with whipped cream and preserve, a choice of sweet from the display and a pot of tea at £5.60. Marples Traditional Cream Tea at £2.35 provides a scone with cream and jam and a pot of tea.

Cakes and scones are all freshly made and there is a wide selection of jams, preserves, marmalades, chutneys, biscuits and handmade chocolates. Freshly ground coffee and speciality teas, including Assam, Ceylon, China, Darjeeling and Earl Grey slake the thirst.

Hours of business:
Mondays to Fridays - 9am to 4.30pm
Saturdays - 9am to 5pm
Sundays - 9.30am to 5pm.

Tea on the Green
3 Eves Corner   Disabled Access
Danbury   Parking - on premises
Essex
CM3 4QF   Tel: 01245 226616

Adjacent to the village green and duck pond in the heart of Danbury village, which is surrounded by National Trust land, Tea on the Green lives up to its name. Inside there is soft pastel décor, floral tablecloths, and fine white bone china with numerous pictures and articles with a sporting or tea and coffee theme. In summer, outside seating adds to the easy atmosphere.

Facilities for the disabled and ample free parking are available. Blakes Wood, Danbury Lakes and Danbury Common are some of the local attractions.

Traditional Cream Tea offers two large scones served warm with strawberry or homemade seasonal preserve and whipped double cream, and a pot of speciality tea for £3.20. A separate menu brings a selection of superb home made cakes, such as lemon sponge cake, dutch apple cake or coffee and walnut cake. Impossible to resist! The Speciality Tea Selection is similarly tempting and extensive!

Consideration is also given to 'Little Adults' with sandwiches filled with delights such as chocolate spread, peanut butter, a child-size slice of cake, and delicious milk shakes and ice cream specials for that extra special treat!

Hours of business:
Mondays to Fridays - 8.30am to 5pm
Saturdays - 10am to 5pm
Sundays - 11am to 5pm
Bank Holidays - 11am to 5pm.

Tea on the Green, Danbury

Corner House Café & Tea Room

47 Undercliffe Road West

Felixstowe

Suffolk

IP11 8AH

Disabled Access

Parking - within 50m

Tel: 01394 283939

The Corner House is set opposite the Leisure Centre and is local to the port, ferry, Languard Fort, the beach and the pier. The tea room is bright, pleasant and welcoming, and the aim is to please the customers with good service and value for money in comfortable surroundings. There is also a large collection of various interesting teapots.

There is no set afternoon tea menu. A wide selection of cakes are freshly baked including coffee, lemon, orange, chocolate and coconut. Home baked scones are served with jam and cream and cherry shortbread. Among the teas are Assam, and Earl Grey. Freshly cooked meals are served all day including breakfast, fish, salads and vegetarian options. Freshly prepared sandwiches are available too.

Hours of business:

Open all year round.

Closed Mondays except Bank Holidays.

Oaks Tearoom
1 Crescent Road   Disabled Access
Felixstowe   Parking - within 50m
Suffolk
IP11 7BY   Tel: 01394 273444

Right in the centre of town in the area known as "The Triangle", opposite
the cinema and just five minutes from the sea front, Oaks Tea Room is
ideal for bracing coastal walks as well as walks in Constable country and
the Nature Reserve, and handy for the Fort-Foot Ferry to Bawdsey Island.

Inside, the atmosphere is bright and cheerful, accentuated by the tall
windows and high ceiling with muslin drapes. Paintings by local artists
adorn the walls and are available for purchase.

Traditional English dishes are served for lunch. The Cream Tea offers two
scones, jam, butter and a pot of tea for £2.95. Be sure to try one of the
speciality butters - Honey, Apple, Lemon or Cinnamon, and make sure you
don't miss the Cake Trolley! Cakes, teacakes and scones are all home
made.

Hours of business:
Mondays to Saturdays - 9am to 5pm
Closed on Sundays and Bank Holidays.

———— oOo ————

Soft yielding minds to water glide away
And sip, with Nymphs, their elemental tea.

(Alexander Pope - Rape of the Lock)

Jemima's Tea Rooms
The Green   Disabled Access
Finchingfield   Parking - within 50m
Essex
CM7 4JX   Tel: 01371 810605

Set in the centre of one of the prettiest villages in England, Jemima's Tea Rooms overlooks the Green and the pond, and is close to the windmill. The four hundred year old building is resplendent with oak beams and a traditional atmosphere, which it shares with its visitors. For the comfort of the guests, this is a non smoking establishment.

Catering for individuals or coach parties, Cream Teas and other variations provide home made scones and cakes for weary travellers, and a choice of Darjeeling and Earl Grey in the pot. The varied menu includes breakfasts, snacks and light lunches as well as afternoon tea, and on Sunday a two course carvery lunch is available.

Hours of business:
Summer:
Mondays to Fridays 10am to 5.30pm
Weekends 10am to 6pm
Winter:
Mondays to Fridays 10am to 4.30pm
Weekends 10am to 5pm.

——— oOo ———

Stands the Church clock at ten to three?
And is there honey still for tea?

(Rupert Brooke 1887 1915)

The Orchard
Mill Way   Disabled Access
Grantchester   Parking - on premises
Cambridge
Cambridgeshire
CB3 9ND   Tel: 01223 845788

The Orchard is something of an institution. Since 1897 people have walked, ridden or punted from Cambridge to have tea. Near to the river, the Meadows, Grantchester village and its church, the tea rooms, too, are an attraction. Rupert Brooke, the poet, wrote the famous line, "Is there honey still for tea?" as a direct reference to Orchard House, where he lived in around 1909.

On sale are Rupert Brooke tapes and books, a range of "Orchard" post cards, and there is a free booklet available which tells of the history of the Orchard. Punt and canoe hire is also available, for a leisurely trip on the river!

A range of light lunches, including sandwiches, jacket potatoes, quiche, home made soups are available in addition to the Afternoon Tea menu. This includes scones with jam and cream, delicious home made cakes, cucumber sandwiches, Twinings speciality teas, and a set afternoon tea is available for just £2.75, or £2.95 if you cannot resist the clotted cream!

Hours of business:
Daily all year - 10am to 6pm.

Millers Cottage Tea Room
Norfolk Lavender Ltd
Caley Mill   Disabled Access
Heacham   Parking - on premises
Norfolk
PE31 7JE   Tel: 01485 570384

This Tea Room, situated in the middle of lavender farm, was built in the mid-1800s as a water powered grain mill. Beamed ceilings bring back the old days when the miller lived here. Millers Cottage is located on the A149 from Kings Lynn.

Lavender sprigged curtains contrast with the dark wood furniture, and in summer months guests can sit outside on the patio to take tea. The olde worlde theme is continued in the menu which offers Lavender Tea, a blend of China and Darjeeling with a Norfolk lavender, providing a fresh and relaxing beverage, with a lavender scone or lavender lemon sponge.

Bread, scones, cakes, jams, pastries, flans, marmalades and chutneys - all are home made and packaged in the kitchens on site, and are available for sale in the Carstone Mill gift shop adjoining, to remind guests of the delicious flavours they enjoyed at tea. A wide choice of teas are on offer.

Hours of business:
All year round - 10am to 5pm
Closed December 25th, 26th and January 1st.

The Ancient House Tea Rooms

Holkham   Disabled Access
Wells-next-the-Sea   Parking - on premises
Norfolk
NR23 1AB   Tel: 01328 711285

The Tea Rooms are located on the A149 coast road at Holkham village, not far from Holkham Hall Estate which is home to the Earl of Lancaster, with easy access to the Hall and also to Holkham beach on Norfolk's north coast. Holkham Hall itself, set in a deer park, is an 18th century Palladian style mansion and is full of artistic and architectural history.

The Ancient House occupies an attractive building which dates back to 1680, and in this wonderfully historic environment, quality home made produce such as Cream Teas, light lunches, savouries, baguettes and main meals are served.

The Cream Tea consists of a scone, butter, cream and jam with a pot of tea or coffee for £3.00, and a range of home made cakes are available. A comprehensive selection of speciality teas, coffee, and cold drinks are on offer, with particular mention of the Holkham Lemon Presse. Definitely one to try!

Hours of business:
Open seven days a week from Easter to end of October - 10.30am to 5.30pm.
From November until Christmas - open weekends only.

The Tea Room

9 East Street   Disabled Access
Kimbolton   Parking   within 50m
Huntingdon
Cambridgeshire
PE18 0HJ   Tel: 01480 860415

The Tea Room is a Mediaeval Hall house situated off the High Street, on the east side of Kimbolton, not far from the Castle where Catherine of Aragon was confined and died in 1536. Also nearby is a 12th century church with Tiffany glass windows.

Inside, low wooden beams complement the white lace tablecloths on the Georgian round tables, and cakes set on bone china are displayed in the Welsh dressers. In the summer there is seating outside in the courtyard where there is always a shaded spot if guests prefer.

Three delicious set afternoon tea menus are available; Traditional Cream Tea, Gateau Tea or Kimbolton Tea which offers a round of sandwiches, choice of fancy cake or a scone with jam and cream, and a pot of tea or a cup of coffee for a reasonable £4.70. These are served all day.

A selection of pastries and fresh cream cakes are available throughout the day, and there is a good variety of teas including Vintage Darjeeling, Earl Grey, Lapsang Souchong and Assam, or treat yourself to their hot chocolate with whipped cream and marshmallow!

Hours of business:
Open only at weekends and Bank Holidays.
Saturdays - 10.30am to 5.30pm
Sundays - 1.30pm to 5.30pm.

Lincoln Cathedral Coffee Shop

Lincoln Cathedral   Disabled Access
Lincoln   Parking - within 100m
Lincolnshire
LN2 1PZ   Tel: 01522 544544

Situated just off the cloisters in the Cathedral under the library, the coffee shop is not far from the beautiful Lincoln Cathedral, the Museum and the historic Bailgate. The Cathedral is close to the shopping centre, and ten minutes away from the Museum of Lincolnshire Life.

Food and drink can be taken outside onto Tennyson Green where seating is available around the statue of Lord Tennyson. In the summer there is also seating in the medieval cloisters.

Cakes and scones are home baked, and a local dish is the mouthwatering Lincolnshire Plum Bread with cheese. Hot meals and light lunches are also served, including traditional fare such as cottage pie with vegetables and Yorkshire pudding.

There is a wide selection of drinks including hot chocolate, cappucino coffee or sparkling elderflower. A real treat is the Lincoln Cathedral wine, sold by the glass with meals, and a speciality here is the 'Cloister Cloud', hot chocolate topped with marshmallow and chocolate. Tea available includes Assam, Ceylon, Darjeeling and Earl Grey.

Hours of business:
Mondays to Saturdays 10am to 4.30pm
Sundays 12 noon to 4.30pm
during summer months.

Frangipani's Tea Rooms
3 Red Lion Square
Stamford   Parking - within 50m
Lincolnshire
PE9 2AH   Tel: 01780 762422

Frangipani's Tea Rooms are set opposite the Square car park, in the picturesque town of Stamford, above Lawsons Photographic. Just fifty metres away, you will find the building used as the doctor's house in the television version of Middlemarch.

The tea rooms are also within easy reach of Burghley House, where The Buccaneers was filmed, and Nene Valley Railway. In 1934, the site was a very popular tea room. Tables are covered with French tablecloths and there is a display of local artists' work. There is a bright and cheerful ambience, complemented by helpful and happy staff.

A varied menu offers Cream Teas, home made cakes, light lunches and sandwiches made to order, and, if time permits, staff willingly prepare an item for a customer if it is not on the menu. In case guests are unable to finish the generous portions, leftovers can be wrapped to take home (doggy bag service). Earl Grey is the favourite tea.

Hours of business:
Mondays to Saturdays - 10am to 5pm.
Closed Sundays.

The Stables Restaurant

Holkham Hall	Disabled Access
Wells next the Sea	Parking - within 100m
Norfolk	
NR23 1AB	Tel: 01328 711648

The Stables Restaurant is in the 19th century stable block, part of the complex of buildings surrounding the magnificent 18th century Palladian style Holkham Hall, one of Britain's most majestic stately homes which is set in a tranquil deer park.

In the Stables Restaurant, display cases with some of the smaller items from the next door Bygones Museum decorate the walls. In warm weather, tea may be taken on the lawn.

Bread, cakes, scones and jams are all home made, many baked on the premises. Along with Clottted Cream Teas, a varied menu of hot and cold fare is offered. Beverages include speciality teas and filter or decaffeinated coffee.

Hours of business:
Open Easter Sunday and Monday.
Open from May Bank Holiday Sunday to end of October.
Sundays to Fridays inclusive 10am to 5.30pm.

——— oOo ———

*Love and scandal are the
best sweetness of tea*

(Henry Fielding)

The Melrose Tea Rooms

The Broadway Centre   Disabled Access
Woodhall Spa   Parking - within 50m
Lincoln
Lincolnshire
LN10 6ST   Tel: 01526 353842

The Melrose Tea Rooms, sited fifty yards from the Golf Hotel, lie within easy reach of the Cottage Museum and near to a walkway to local woodlands where kinema in the woods can be found. The Dambuster Memorial is close by.

The interior of the Tea Rooms is pleasantly set out, with a pastel green carpet, decorated walls and pine furniture. Waitress and waiter service brings your tea to your table, while you can watch the chef in traditional whites, preparing your order.

Afternoon Tea provides a fruit or plain scone with jam, cream and a pot of tea, and is very reasonably priced at £1.45. Otherwise, there is a large selection of speciality cakes. The menu, which includes special lunches, is served throughout the day, with all food cooked to order. The savoury dishes are all home made and locally grown salads and vegetables are used.

Hours of business:
Mondays to Saturdays - 10am to 5pm
Sundays - 11am to 5pm
Open all year seven days a week.

South East

Poppies Tea Rooms
37 Stert Street   Disabled Access
Abingdon   Parking - within 50m
Oxfordshire

                                             Tel: 01235 526660

Poppies is opposite the Yorkshire Bank in the centre of Abingdon. It is also close to the Town Hall and museum, the river Thames, the Medieval Abbey and Abbey Meadows, all places to see in Abingdon.

The listed building is typically English with oak beams, and the décor is kept to look traditional, although the warmth is provided by the wonders of modern central heating! Two rooms cater for smokers and non smokers and the service is friendly, polite and efficient. Food is always prepared to order in the fastest time possible. A garden is also available for afternoon tea in warmer weather.

Afternoon Tea comprises a pot of tea for one, served with two freshly baked fruit scones, fresh cream and home made jam. Much of the produce is home made and there is a vast choice to whet the appetite. Fruit cake, cherry sponge, date and walnut loaf, flapjack and shortbread are just some of the many delicacies available.

There is also an extensive list of ice creams with flavours ranging from Bavarian black cherry and brown bread to chocolate trufito and white bombe. Teas include Assam, Ceylon and Earl Grey.

Hours of business:
Mondays to Saturdays - 9.30am to 4.30pm.

The Balcombe Tea Rooms
Bramble Hill   Disabled Access
Balcombe   Parking - on premises
West Sussex
RH17 6HR   Tel: 01444 811777

Set in the village centre in a popular walking and cycling area close to the viaduct, Balcombe Lake, Ardingley Reservoir, High Beech Gardens, Nymans Gardens and Borde Hill Gardens, The Balcombe Tea Rooms are located in a designated area of outstanding beauty. Close by is the local railway station, which enables non drivers to gain easy access to this beautiful area.

Clotted Cream Tea presents a pot of tea, two home made scones, jam and clotted cream. Cakes and scones are home baked, and the tea rooms specialise in old fashioned bread pudding, fresh cream cakes and raspberries and strawberries in season. Not to be forgotten are the iced carrot cake, the Yum Yum Cake or the fresh cream meringues.

On sale are local honey, home made jams and marmalades and locally made crafts. On sunny days, afternoon tea may be enjoyed on the sunny patio. Among the teas are Assam, Darjeeling, Earl Grey and Lapsang.

Hours of business:
Tuesdays to Saturdays - 10.30am to 5pm
Sundays - 2pm to 5.30pm
Bank Holidays - 10.30am to 5pm
Closed from Christmas to end of January.

Sea Cottage Tea Shoppe
Marine Drive   Disabled Access
Barton on Sea   Parking   on premises
Hampshire
BH25 7DZ   Tel: 01425 614086

On a cliff top overlooking The Needles and the Isle of Wight, the Tea Shoppe has traditional cosy cottage décor and presents the healthier food options which have won proprietors Kevin and Wendy Noon a Healthy Heartbeat Award for three consecutive years. Sea Cottage is well positioned for the beach, with views across the Solent, in an area known for its fossils.

An excellent range of nautically themed Afternoon Teas are on the menu, including Full Sail, Portside, High Tide and Low Tide, providing very adequate choice for the guests. Full Sail replenishes guests after a hearty walk with a pot of tea, a sandwich, two home made scones, jam and clotted cream for £4.25. Speciality teas are available, and all the fare is home made, including the scones, sponges, pies and tarts.

Special themed party events can be arranged in this superb location, and the menu also includes lunches and light meals which are all home cooked, morning coffees and a delicious three course Sunday lunch.

Hours of business;
Tuesdays to Fridays - 10.30am to 5pm
Saturdays and Sundays - 10am to 5pm
Open Bank Holidays
Open until 7pm during the summer months
Closed on Mondays and during January.

The Old Tea House
7 Windsor End
Beaconsfield
Buckinghamshire
HP9 2JJ

Disabled Access
Parking - within 50m

Tel: 01494 676273

Set opposite the Church in the picturesque old town of Beaconsfield, The Old Tea House is a Grade I listed building, with internal brick exposed walls, beamed ceilings and a Tudor façade. It enjoys views over Beaconsfield old town.

Inside, tables are set with tablecloths, white tableware and fresh flowers. At the back is a conservatory overlooking a walled garden. Local attractions are the Bekonscot Model Village, the Odds Farm Rare Breed Centre, Wycombe Chair Museum and the Chiltern Open Air Museum.

On offer is a selection of cakes, home made to traditional and new family recipes. Carrot and banana, fresh cream raspberry jam sponge, and sticky gingerbread are just three that should be sampled and there are many more that are equally delicious!

Speciality sandwiches and Cornish Clotted Cream Teas are highlights of the menu. Numerous teas are on offer along with three blends of coffee. The menu also provides home made soups and light lunches.

Hours of business:
All year - Tuesdays to Saturdays - 9am to 5pm.
Closed for two weeks over Christmas period.

Royal Oak Farm Tea Room

Royal Oak Farm   Disabled Access
Beckley   Parking - on premises
Oxfordshire
OX3 9TY   Tel: 01865 351246

Set in a suntrap on the edge of bluebell woods, peaceful and tranquil, you will find Royal Oak Farm Tea Room, on the B4027. Attached to the farm, there is an animal garden, with lots of friendly goats, sheep and pigs, and farm shop on the premises. Plenty of outdoor seating is available for the warmer days.

Everything on the menu is home made including the Cream Tea, which consists of two scones, jam, cream and a pot of tea for just £2.85. The rest of the menu offers light lunches, quiche, soup, rolls and "Happy Hen" boiled eggs, all served throughout the day. To follow, there is a wide variety of delicious home made cakes.

Hours of business:
Open Easter to end of August -
Saturdays, Sundays and Bank Holidays 10.30am to 6pm
Also Mondays to Fridays in July and August 11.30am to 5.30pm.

———— oOo ————

Venus her myrtle, Phoebus has his bays;
Tea both excels, which she vouchsafes to praise..
The Muses' friend, tea doth our fancy aid,
Repress those vigours which the head invade,
And keeps that palace of the soul serene.

(Edmund Waller)

Claris's
1-3 High Street   Disabled Access
Biddenden   Parking - within 50m
Nr Ashford
Kent
TN27 8AL   Tel: 01580 291025

Part of a row of fifteenth century Grade I listed buildings facing the village green, Claris's is near to the Biddenden Vineyards and the home of the famous Siamese twins, the Biddenden Maids, Eliza and Mary Chulkhurst, who were born in the year 1100. Local attractions include the Kent and East Sussex light railway, Sissinghurst Castle Gardens and Leeds Castle.

Low oak beams and two inglenook fireplaces create an atmosphere of cosy homeliness where lace cloths and white china cover spacious tables. The patio garden is a popular summer feature. There is a no smoking policy throughout.

Home made cakes and savouries are served throughout the day, along with sandwiches, ploughmans and salads. The Cream Teas and meringues with fresh local cream are irresistible! Teas include Assam, Ceylon, Darjeeling and Earl Grey.

A founder member of the prestigious Tea Council Guild of Tea Shops, Claris's takes great pride in the quality and selection of teas that are served.

Hours of business:
Tuesdays to Sundays - 10.30am to 5.20pm
Closed for 3 weeks in January.

Park House Tea Room & Antiques

26 Park Street   Disabled Access
Bladon   Parking - on premises
Oxfordshire
OX20 1RW   Tel: 01993 812817

Approximately one mile from the famous Blenheim Palace, Park House provides a period setting with antique tables and chairs in which to enjoy your tea in a non smoking environment. Inexpensive antiques and gifts can be purchased.

The outside seating area provides a comfortable and refreshing place to take tea in summer months, and the decorated toilet facilities are often commented on!

Afternoon Tea comprises cheese and cucumber sandwiches with salad garnish, coleslaw and potato salad, followed by fruit cake, scone with clotted cream and preserve with a pot of tea for £4.90.

Baguettes and sandwiches, light lunches, crumpets, English muffins and cakes are other selections from the menu. Don't miss the delicious home made fruit cake! Teas include Assam, Ceylon, Darjeeling and Earl Grey.

Hours of business:
Open all year every day -
Winter 10am to 5pm
Summer 9am to 6pm.

Knollys
Bodiam   Disabled Access
Robertsbridge   Parking - on premises
East Sussex
TN32 5UD   Tel: 01580 830323

Situated in an area of outstanding natural beauty, the tea room and garden adjoin and have direct access to the castle and grounds of Bodiam castle, opposite the village green. Egon Ronay recommended, Knollys are shortly to be featured in Meridian Television's "Al Fresco Eating". Tables and chairs are available in the Rose Garden so you may sit in the sunshine and enjoy your meal. There is also a craft and gift shop.

Cream Tea serves a pot of tea with two scones, strawberry jam and cream, with waitress service. High Tea offers salmon and cucumber, or prawn salad sandwiches with home made, fresh cream cake and a pot of tea.

Cakes and scones are home baked, and specialities to tempt the palate include pavlova, passion cake, apricot pie and chocolate cake. For a real treat, try the fudge cake with fresh cream or ice cream! Local strawberries are also available in season. Among the teas are Assam, Darjeeling, Earl Grey and Lapsang.

Hours of business:
Tuesdays to Saturdays 10.30am to 5pm
Sundays - 10.30am to 5.30pm
Closed on Mondays except Bank Holidays
Closed from October to just before Easter.

The Tea House

17 High Street
Borough Green
Sevenoaks
Kent
TN15 7QE

Disabled Access
Parking within 50m

Tel: 01732 883073

The Tea House building dates from the 18th century, with Victorian additions when it became a butchers shop for a while. Wooden beams and open fires in winter create a traditional atmosphere.

The Tea House Afternoon Special provides a pot of tea with a scone, jam and cream, a choice of sandwiches and home made cake. Cakes, scones and jams are home made, house favourites being chocolate fudge, meringues and cream cakes, and there is a large round table laden with delicious cakes from which to choose.

Among the teas are Assam, Darjeeling and Earl Grey. Highchairs are available for children, and there are designated smoking and non smoking areas.

Hours of business:
Open Tuesdays to Saturdays inclusive - 10am to 4.30pm.
Closed on Sundays and Mondays.

Thank God for tea!
What would the world do without tea?
How did it exist?
I am glad that I was not born before tea.

(Sidney Smith, 1771-1845)

Penny Plain Tea Room and Garden

44 High Street   Disabled Access
Brading   Parking - within 50m
Isle of Wight
PO36 0DN   Tel: 01983 407649

Situated opposite the old Town Hall with a view of the old town stocks, Penny Plain Tea Room is not far from the Isle of Wight Wax Museum and Lilliput Dolls' Museum.

The quaint tea room atmosphere is enhanced by twenties and thirties dance music, and in warm weather, guests can sit out in the large patio garden.

Scones and gateaux are home made, while in season, cream teas serve up fresh strawberries and clotted cream. Among other house specials, are the hot scotch pancakes with real maple syrup and double cream, topped with roast almonds. Tea or coffee is available, the teas including Darjeeling and Earl Grey.

Hours of business:
Daily 11am to 5pm
Closed November to March.

Mushroom Sandwiches (for ten)

Stew ten mushrooms with black pepper, lemon juice and salt, two red chillies, one egg and one gill of milk. Add two large tomatoes, half an ounce of breadcrumbs, half an onion and mash together.

(Five O'Clock Tea, 1886)

Manor Farm Tea Rooms

Ringwood Road   Disabled Access
Burley   Parking - on premises
New Forest
Hampshire
BH24 4AB   Tel: 01425 402218

Manor Farm Tea Rooms are in an original thatched cottage, established in 1904. Original oak beams, inglenook fireplace and log fire during the winter make this a cosy place to take tea.

Cream Tea consists of two scones, blackcurrant jam and clotted cream with tea or coffee. Hampshire High Tea offers a savoury sandwich, two slices of bread and butter, a scone with blackcurrant jam and clotted cream, cake and tea or coffee.

Renowned for the home made scones and the jams that are made to the specifications of the proprietors, Peter and Kathy Hunt, bread and cakes are also home baked, and teas available include Assam, Ceylon, China, Darjeeling and Earl Grey.

Hours of business:
Winter season - closed all day Monday
Summer season (from end of May) - closed Mondays mornings only.

Tea-time

4A High Street	Disabled Access
Chalfont St Giles	Parking - within 100m
Buckinghamshire	
HP8 4QP	Tel: 01494 871099

Tea-time is located on the village green, in a pretty and unspoilt village setting, not far from the National Trust cottage where the poet John Milton lived, which now houses a museum.

Visitors are welcomed with a choice of menu. The Traditional Tea comprises two scones with whipped cream, preserve and a pot of tea, while the Village Tea includes sandwiches and a choice of either scones with cream and jam, or a cake, with a pot of tea. Scones and cakes are home made and the range of teas include Assam, Earl Grey and Darjeeling.

Breakfast, morning coffee, snacks and lunches are also catered for, and a take away service is available.

Hours of business:
Mondays to Saturdays - 10am to 5.50pm
Sundays - 1pm to 5.50pm.

St Martin's Tea Rooms
3 St Martin's Street
Chichester
West Sussex
PO19 1NP

Disabled Access
Parking - within 50m

Tel: 01243 786715

St Martin's Tea Rooms are set in the middle of an historic city. The large double fronted medieval building with Georgian frontage has been carefully restored, and Keith Nelson, the proprietor, has spent the last twenty years personally preserving the character of the building. Three log fires, genuine oak beams and the medieval surroundings create a wonderful atmosphere for afternoon tea. Outside, there is a pretty brick paved garden.

He has also ensured that food and drink is of the highest quality. Healthy eating is a priority with Heartbeat Award for Healthiest Food and Preparation given by the local Environmental Health Department. To ensure this high quality, no tinned or convenience foods are used, cooking is not done in aluminium pots or pans or in microwave ovens.

Organic bread, cakes and scones are all home baked and all ingredients are written out for the items, which include carrot yoghurt cake, nutty fruit flapjack and banana bread. The wide range of teas include among its number Assam, Ceylon, China, Darjeeling, Earl Grey and many more.

Hours of business:
Mondays to Saturdays - 9am to 6pm
Closed on Sundays and Bank Holidays.

Annie's Country Pantry

22 New Street   Disabled Access
Chipping Norton   Parking - within 50m
Oxfordshire

                                       Tel: 01608 641100

Annie's Country Pantry is close to local attractions such as The Rollright Stones, Chasterton House, the local Museum, the almshouses and Pool Meadow, a naturalist's haven.

The tea room is in part of an old Cotswold stone house called Hill Lawn Manor, and your afternoon tea may be enjoyed at one of the marble topped tables. Major Dunlop, the local vet, lived in the manor in 1920.

Amongst the menu of breakfasts, light lunches and afternoon teas, Full English Tea offers Edwardian Sandwich, cake, a scone with butter and jam, and a pot of tea for less than five pounds. Or you may select Cream Tea, which consists of two homemade scones, jam and cream for less than three pounds.

Cakes, scones and jams are home made, and bread from the local baker is used to make the sandwiches. Earl Grey, Darjeeling and Lapsang Souchong are the main teas on offer and freshly ground coffee is always available.

Hours of business:
Mondays to Saturdays 9am to 5pm
Closed on Sundays.

The Tea Shop
Old Pottery Buildings   Disabled Access
Down Lane   Parking - on premises
Compton
Surrey
GU3 1DQ   Tel: 01483 811030

The Tea Shop building, adjacent to Watts Gallery, is almost a hundred years old and the décor is random as regular customers like it that way! Alongside are found Pilgrims Way and Watts Memorial Chapel and in the village, a 10th century church.

Sally and Timothy Porter are a mother and son partnership who have been in the Egon Ronay Guide since 1987. There is access for the disabled, although there is one step up to The Tea Shop.

The Tea Shop provides a very comprehensive tea list of approximately 30 types of tea plus numerous herbal teas, with the House Tea being Taylors Yorkshire Gold, a very good quality Indian tea. All cakes and scones are made on the premises using free range eggs, traditional methods and ingredients. Also home made is the Tea Shop Jam, which gets superb reviews! Hot food, such as their speciality, Welsh Rarebit, and delicious toasted sandwiches are also available, and very hard to resist is the Meadow Cottage Farms Jersey Ice Cream in a range of scrumptious flavours.

A range of the home made cakes and fourteen flavours of the ice cream are available to take away from the Tea Shop's own shop.

Hours of business:
Daily - 10.30am to 5.30pm.
Closed 24th to 31st December inclusive.

Dickens Tea Cottage
5 South Street
Eastbourne   Parking - within 50m
Sussex

Tel: 01323 732637

Established in 1946, Dickens Tea Cottage is managed by Penelope and
George Kyprianou and is located in an attractive eighteenth century
building close to the town centre, sea and theatres. Oak beams, prints, and,
in winter, an open fire, create a relaxing atmosphere which is
complemented by fine china and a friendly waitress service. It is easy to
believe that Charles Dickens once visited.

Special Sussex Cream Tea, or Tea and Cake make a reasonably priced treat
and there is a choice of China and Earl Grey tea. Scones, cakes and pies
are baked on the premises, with an accent on old fashioned cakes such as
Melting Moments.

Hours of business:
Closed on Sundays and Mondays.

——— oOo ———

In Endymion, I leaped headlong into the sea,
and thereby have become better acquainted with
the surroundings, the quicksands, and the rocks,
than if I had stayed upon the green shore,
and piped a silly pipe,
and took tea and comfortable advice.

(John Keats)

Clara's
9 High Street
East Hoathly Parking - within 50m
Nr Lewes
East Sussex
BN8 6DR Tel: 01825 840339

Clara's is situated in the middle of a quiet bypassed village close to the church, the pottery, and opposite the house of Thomas Turner, diarist 1754-1765, and copies of his diaries are for sale in the shop. Oak beams are testimony to the fact that the building dates from about 1760.

Disabled access is restricted by the two steps up into the tea room, although it is situated on the ground floor.

Cakes, scones and jam are home made, and Cream Tea comprises a pot of tea for one, two scones, butter, jam and cream. Clara's Special offers a pot of tea, toasted buttered teacake with cream and jam. The main teas are Darjeeling and Earl Grey. As well as food, Clara's sells home made jams and chutneys, a wide range of gifts, cards, bric a brac and Rowan knitting yarns.

Hours of business:
Wednesdays to Saturdays 10.30am to 5pm
Sundays and Bank Holiday Mondays - 2pm - 5pm.
Closed for approximately 2 to 3 weeks after Christmas.

Flintstones Tea Room

The Quay   Disabled Access
South Street
Emsworth
Hampshire
PO10 7EQ   Tel: 01243 377577

Flintstones is a family run tea room in a 17th century flint building on Emsworth quay which overlooks picturesque Chichester Harbour. The tea room is opposite the sailing club. There is a popular area around the millpond adjacent to Langstone Harbour.

The distinctive interior is typical of a traditional tea room. The varied menu offers pasta dishes, home made soup, ploughmans lunches, home made cakes, tea cakes and ice cream to name just a few items. The Cream Tea is priced at a reasonable £3.25, and in warmer weather, customers may choose a cooling flavoured iced drink or an ice cream to follow their delicious home made scone.

Hours of business:
Every day of the week.

——— oOo ———

THE POETS AT TEA (MACAULAY)

Pour, valet, pour the water,
The water steaming hot!
A spoonful for each man of us,
Another for the pot!

Barry Pain
1864-1928

The Smithy Tea Rooms

Exbury Gardens   Disabled Access
Exbury   Parking - on premises
Southampton
Hampshire
SO45 1AZ   Tel: 01703 898737

The Smithy Tea Rooms are conveniently situated adjoining the plant
centre and entrance to Exbury Gardens. A former blacksmiths forge has
been skilfully converted into the Tea Rooms; the building retains much of
its former character.

The remarkable two hundred acre woodland garden, created by Lionel de
Rothschilds, overlooks Beaulieu River. In Spring, there are spectacular
displays of rhododendrons, azaleas, camellias and magnolias. Other local
attractions include Beaulieu Motor Museum, Bucklers Hard Maritime
Museum and Lepe Beach, and of course, the beautiful New Forest itself
with its famous wild ponies.

A splendid menu offers three choices for Afternoon Tea; Exbury Clotted
Cream Tea for £3.95, two fresh scones with Cornish Clotted Cream,
strawberry preserve and a pot of tea, or Gardeners Tea for £2.95, freshly
baked cake and a pot of tea, or Homewood Tea for £4.95, a round of
freshly prepared sandwiches, and freshly baked cake and a pot of tea. The
cakes are delicious and irresistible! Try the St Clements fresh orange and
lemon cake, or the Classic coffee and walnut; home made using natural
ingredients. Speciality teas, coffees and herbal teas are also available.

Hours of business:
Daily - 10am to 5pm.
Closed November to February inclusive.

Charlotte Emily's Victorian Tea Rooms
2-4 Old High Street   Disabled Access
Folkestone   Parking - within 50m
Kent
CT20 1RL   Tel: 01303 220732

These beautiful traditional Tea Rooms and restaurant are located some way from the main High Street, and not far from the harbour. Nearby are the historic cobbled streets of Folkestone with traditional shops.

As the name hints, the tea rooms have a Victorian theme, with waitresses dressed in Victorian style, offering an exceptional standard of service. Having been established since 1989, Charlotte Emily's is a family run business serving traditional English cuisine of a very high standard with most items being cooked fresh each day.

The extensive menu offers a superb range from English Breakfasts, lunches, fresh sandwiches, home made roast dinners, vegetarian meals, a special children's menu and of course, the traditional cream teas. Egg and cucumber sandwiches, fruit scone with fresh whipped cream and jam, a pot of tea or filter coffee and a cake of your choice is too tempting for words, and represents good value at £4.95!

Not forgetting the patisserie, which offers such delights as Death by Chocolate, Passion Cake and Coffee and Walnut cake, and a splendid range of teas and coffees, it is easy to think one has slipped back in time!

Hours of business:
Daily - 9am to 6pm
Closed only on Boxing Day and New Years Day.

The Old World Tea Gardens

High Street   Disabled Access
Godshill   Parking - within 50m
Isle of Wight
Hampshire
PO38 3HZ   Tel: 01983 840637

Set opposite the Chapel in the village centre, The Old World Tea Gardens are local to the ancient church on the hill, the model village, toy museum and Natural History Centre. Attached to a sixteenth century thatched cottage, there is a large tea garden for your enjoyment in the warmer weather. Parking is available on the premises for coaches, and within 50 metres for cars.

Cream Tea, for £3.00, comprises a pot of tea or coffee, or a cold drink, with two home made scones, jam and a choice of whipped or clotted cream. Strawberry meringue glacé in season, knickerbocker glories, fruit cakes and a selection of other cakes are among the home made specials.

In addition to these, Mr and Mrs Saunders, the proprietors, also offer a diabetic cream tea. Earl Grey and Carisbrooke blend are among the beverages on offer.

Hours of business:
Daily - 10am to 5.30pm
Closed from November to February.

Willow Tree Tea Gardens & Restaurant

High Street   Disabled Access
Godshill   Parking - within 100m
Isle of Wight
PO38 3HZ   Tel: 01983 840633

Willow Tree Tea Gardens is situated in the centre of the historic village of Godshill, 100 metres from the free car park. The beautiful sheltered gardens complete with fountain, which have been completely redesigned for 1998, provide a sun trap during the summer months where customers can enjoy tea. Well behaved dogs are allowed in the gardens. Inside are large separate smoking and non smoking dining rooms.

In the locality, places of interest include Godshill Church, Godshill Model Village, the Doll Museum and the Herb Gardens.

The menu is varied and traditional. Cream Teas, a selection of home made cakes and puddings, freshly made sandwiches and baguettes, and a range of light lunches are all on offer.

Cream Tea consists of two large home made scones, jam, butter, a large portion of whipped cream and a pot of tea. Bread and cakes are also home baked, with house specials including deep apple pie, lemon meringue pie, and strawberry cream tarts made from local strawberries and fresh cream. Earl Grey and Kenya are among the teas on offer.

Hours of business:
Open seven days a week from end of March until first or second week of November.
Closed from mid November to end of March.

Peter de Wit's Café
21 Greenwich Church Street   Disabled Access
Greenwich   Parking - within 50m
London
SE10 9BJ   Tel: 0181 305 0048

Peter de Wit's Café, a listed building dating back to 1710, is situated in the heart of Greenwich, known for its sights such as the Greenwich Observatory, Maritime Museum, the Cutty Sark, as well as the park and the weekend markets. The Café is located right next to a bus stop which will take you directly into central London.

White bone china and a curious collection of chairs and tables create the décor, in addition to a variety of hand made wooden objects which are for sale.

The atmosphere here is relaxed and friendly, the staff are young, and are mostly students or artists who endeavour to assist their customers however they can; calling for a taxi, checking theatre times, heating baby's bottle or looking up railway timetables.

Cream Teas offer a large scone, jam, Cornish Cream (as used by the Ritz) and a pot of tea or other beverage. Specialities include traditional cakes and pastries, which are all home made. Sandwiches are made to the individual guest's requirements. The wide range of teas include Assam, Ceylon, China, Darjeeling and Earl Grey.

Hours of business:
Mondays to Fridays - 11am to 6pm
Saturdays - 10am to 7pm
Sundays - 9.30am to at least 7pm.

The Village Tea Rooms
High Street
Hamble   Parking - within 100m
Southampton
Hampshire
SO31 4HA   Tel: 01703 455583

The Village Tea Rooms are located at the top of the High Street in Hamble Square, a delightful and peaceful place to stop for tea. The television series, Howards Way, was set in and around Hamble, and the Tea Rooms themselves made an appearance or two! In the area, you can find river trips on the River Hamble, scenic walks in the Royal Victoria Country Park, and visit Bursledon Windmill.

The Tea Rooms are set in late 18th century buildings which were originally a rope makers and coffin makers workshop. The first floor room features the exposed beams of the original loft. The building is reputed to be haunted, and on quiet days the proprietor has been known to tell a ghost story or two!

For afternoon tea, treat yourself to a delicious Hamble Cream Special; two scones with cream and jam, and tea or coffee all for just £2.95. Light lunches are also served, and all cakes are home baked by the proprietor, Mrs Pullen. In the warmer weather, the attractive tea gardens are the perfect place to while away the hours, and before you leave, you may find the perfect present to take home in the Gift Shop, with the range including local crafts, 'Hamble' china, thimbles and a selection of books and leaflets featuring local attractions and walks.

Hours of business:
Open seven days a week (closed Christmas Day).
Winter opening - 9am to 5pm
Summer opening (Easter to October) - 7.30am to 6pm.

Norton House Olde English Teahouse

The High Street   Disabled Access
Henfield   Parking - on premises
West Sussex
BN5 9DB   Tel: 01273 492064

Located near the home of the Sussex Wildlife Trust Headquarters "Woodsmill", and the South Downs, Norton House Olde English Teahouse is ideal for enthusiastic walkers taking a break. The timbered house with Queen Anne façade was restored in 1968/69 by its present owners.

It is furnished with traditional oak tables and chairs, which complement the old brick fireplaces and wooden beams and there is a delightful old English garden where refreshments can be served in summer weather.

Cream Tea, served in delightful English Bone China, comprises two scones with butter, jam, cream and tea. Also available are Plain Tea, Scone Tea, Cake Tea and Boiled Egg Tea. Specialities include home made meringues, rock cakes plus eight other varieties of home made cakes, and not forgetting Norton House Bread.

To wash it down, there is a choice of PG Tips, Camomile, Darjeeling, Earl Grey, Keemun or Lapsang. On hot days, a Norton House Iced Coffee with ice cream and fresh cream is a cooling alternative.

Hours of business:
Thursdays to Mondays - 10am to 5pm.
Closed on Tuesdays and Wednesdays.
Open all year.

Crispins Restaurant & Tearooms

Bridge House   Disabled Assistance
52 Hart Street   Parking - within 50m
Henley on Thames
Oxfordshire
RG9 2AU   Tel: 01491 574232

Adjacent to Henley Bridge and opposite the Red Lion Hotel, Bridge House is an elegant Grade II Listed Georgian building. Overlooking the Thames, it is well positioned for the Royal Regatta and boating activities all year round. Local attractions include the boating and walks along the River Thames, and the River and Rowing Museum.

Inside, potted palms and overmantel mirrors adorn the buttermilk walls, the mahogany bar and entrance doors reflect the period, and light classical music helps to create an Edwardian ambience unique to Crispins. Proprietor Rodney Newbold offers personal, friendly and helpful service alongside the staff.

Cream Tea provides hungry rowers with two home made scones, jam, butter and fresh cream, a pot of tea and a fresh cream chocolate éclair. Specialities include meringue glacé, home made apple pie or chocolate cake, caramel shortbreads and home made pies and pastries. A good selection of speciality teas offers Assam, Ceylon, China, Darjeeling and Earl Grey, and excellent coffees are available too.

Hours of business:
Tuesdays to Fridays - afternoons only
Saturdays and Sundays - 10am to 7.30pm
Extended hours during summer season and always open on Bank Holidays.

The Coffee Shop
Jardineric Garden Centre   Disabled Access
Studley Green   Parking - on premises
High Wycombe
Buckinghamshire
HP14 3UX   Tel: 01494 485965

Located in a garden centre close to West Wycombe village and House, The Coffee Shop is surrounded by good walking countryside. Proprietor Christine Smith offers a light, bright plant filled room, with a courtyard setting in the summer.

In addition to home made cakes and scones, teas such as Assam, Darjeeling and Earl Grey are served. Hot and cold lunches and snacks are also available.

Hours of business:
Mondays to Saturdays - 9.30am to 4.30pm
Sundays - 10.30am to 4.30pm

——— oOo ——

THE POETS AT TEA
(TENNYSON)

I think that I am drawing to an end:
For on a sudden came a gasp for breath,
And stretching of the hands, and blinded eyes,
And a great darkness falling on my soul.
O Hallelujah!.....Kindly pass the milk.

Barry Pain
1864-1928

Elan Arts Centre
Sundridge Road
Ide Hill   Disabled Access
Sevenoaks   Parking - within 50m
Kent
TN14 6JT   Tel: 01732 750344

Set opposite the green at the roundabout, Elan Arts Centre is well-known as a unique gift shop with the watercolours and oil paintings of many local artists on view throughout the shop and tea room, with the exhibits being changed monthly. The beautiful patio garden features hanging baskets and troughs in abundance.

Local attractions include Emmetts Garden, Chiddingstone Castle, and Knole House; all within fifteen minutes drive by car.

There is no set menu for Afternoon Tea; the customer is free to choose their own combination from the wonderful array of home made cakes, biscuits and scones. The scones alone are varied, with wholewheat fruit, apple, walnut and ginger or cheese to choose from.

The home made fare includes all of the soups, savouries, cakes, scones, biscuits, jams and marmalades. To complement the menu, speciality teas including Assam, Darjeeling, Ceylon, Earl Grey and Kenyan are available.

Hours of business:
Wednesdays to Sundays - 10am to 5.30pm
Closed on Mondays and Tuesdays.
Closed from Christmas Day until mid-February.

Dippins Tea Rooms
2 Church Street
Kintbury   Parking - within 50m
Berkshire
RG17 9TR   Tel: 01488 657522

Dippins Tea Rooms are located on the first floor, above the butchers and estate agents, where one can look out across Kintbury and watch the comings and goings of the locals. At the end of Church Street is the historic St Mary's Church and beyond is the Kennet and Avon Canal where you can stroll along the peaceful towpath alongside the beautifully painted barges.

The tea rooms are traditionally decorated with plenty of nick-nacks and pictures to look at. Cream Teas and Afternoon Teas are served with a De-Luxe Tea for Two consisting of a selection of sandwiches, scones, cream and jam, delicious home made cake, home made biscuits and tea or coffee for £8.95.

Dippins pride themselves on their quality teas and coffees, the Belgian chocolates and their scrumptious home made cakes and biscuits, and the proprietor, Joanne Saunders, also offers a range of gifts, quality preserves and a gift and hamper service.

Hours of business:
Tuesdays to Fridays - 10am to 5pm
Saturdays - 10am to 5.30pm
Sundays - 12 noon to 5.30pm
Mondays - closed (except Bank Holidays).

Lamberhurst Tea Rooms

The Down   Disabled Access
Lamberhurst   Parking - on premises
Kent
TN3 8ES   Tel: 01892 890891

Opposite Lamberhurst Vineyard on the B2100 Lamberhurst to Wadhurst road, Lamberhurst Tea Rooms are close to the National Trust property Scotney Castle, and Bayham Abbey ruins, run by English Heritage. Also nearby are Owl House Gardens and Bewl Water.

The 18th century property, which faces the Down, and is surrounded by beautiful countryside, was built as four cottages, and retains the wooden beam, two inglenook fireplaces, and a cosy yet elegant ambience. There is lovely private tea garden in which to enjoy summer afternoon tea. The staff are especially friendly and helpful, and it is evident that the proprietor, Christine Dickens and her staff concentrate on quality of service.

The tables are decked with pretty linen tablecloths, tasteful cutlery, and bone china throughout. Nora Batty Tea offers a pot of tea or cafetiere of coffee, Lardy Cake and a home made cake. Gourmet Tea comprises tea or coffee, along with assorted sandwiches, scone, butter, jam and cream, and home made cake. Bread, cakes, scones and jams are home made with traditional tea breads, rich farm milk and cream, and delicious Devon ice cream. Speciality teas include Assam, Darjeeling and Earl Grey; loose leaf tea is available.

Hours of business:
May to October - Wednesdays to Saturdays 10.30am to 5.30pm and Sundays 12 noon to 5.30pm
March, April, November and December - weekends only
January and February - closed
Mondays and Tuesdays closed (except Bank Holiday Mondays).

The Mad Hatter Tea Rooms

10 High Street   Disabled Access
Lyndhurst   Parking - within 50m
Hampshire
SO43 7BD   Tel: 01703 282341

The Tea Rooms are situated opposite the Crown Hotel in Lyndhurst, and below the Church, the burial place of Lewis Carroll's real life Alice, Alice Liddell. The Mad Hatter Tea Rooms are within walking distance of the New Forest, and within easy reach are Brockenhurst, Beaulieu and Lymington, all well worth a visit.

There is a roof garden where tea can be enjoyed in fine weather, and inside the tea rooms the Alice in Wonderland theme continues with the 'backward clocks'! The Cream Tea consists of two delicious farmhouse scones with jam and clotted cream with a pot of tea. Scones are home made, plain, fruit and date and walnut.

An extensive range of cakes is on offer, and hard to resist is the selection at the patisserie cabinet! A good choice of light lunches, snacks and desserts are available, and thoughtfully provided is a 'Children's Lunchtime Specials' section on the menu. For the early birds, another speciality here is the Full English Breakfast.

The teapot is definitely not home to the Dormouse in this establishment, but visitors can enjoy teas such as Assam, Darjeeling and Earl Grey.

Hours of business
Open seven days a week - hours according to customer demand
Closed for annual holiday and/or refurbishments during November or January - telephone to check.

Burgers of Marlow

The Causeway

Marlow

Buckinghamshire

SL7 1NF

Disabled Access

Parking - within 50m

Tel: 01628 483389

Set in a seventeenth century listed building at the bottom of Marlow High Street, and close to the Bridge, church and park, Burgers of Marlow boasts bay windows, oak beams and wood block flooring, and also the comfort of air conditioning. There is open access from the tea room to the chocolate shop and bakery.

The tea room is run by the Burger family, who offer a well priced menu for their cream teas. A pot of Yorkshire blend tea is served with home made scones, whipped cream, preserve and a cake from the selection table.

There is a selection of home made cakes and pastries, and types of tea include Assam, Ceylon, China, Earl Grey and Darjeeling. A wide range of soft drinks and hot beverages is available. A further menu of cooked dishes is available including rarebits and egg dishes, together with salad, pies and soup.

Hours of business:

Mondays to Saturdays - 8.30am to 5.30pm.

Closed on Sundays and all public holidays.

Old Mint Coffee House

New Road Baptist Church   Disabled Access
Bonn Square
Oxford
Oxfordshire
OX1 8LQ   Tel: 01865 250134

The Old Mint Coffee House took its name from its building which used to be a money mint in the time of Charles I. It is right in the heart of Oxford, giving visitors easy access to the University, St Mary's Church tower and the Radcliffe Camera. In days gone by, the site of the New Road Baptist Church has itself been the site of shootings and clashes between Baptists and other religions.

Cream Tea offers two home made scones, jam and cream plus a pot of tea for £2.75. Many other tempting home made cakes, pastries and other hot and cold dishes can be found on the menu.

Hours of business:
Mondays to Saturdays - 9.30am to 5pm.

—— oOo ——

THE POETS AT TEA
(MACAULAY)

The cosy fire is bright and gay,
The merry kettle boils away
And hums a cheerful song.
I sing the saucer and the cup;
Pray, Mary, fill teapot up,
and do not make it strong.

Barry Pain
1864 - 1928

The Coach House Tearooms

108A Old London Road	Disabled Access
Patcham Village	Parking - within 50m
Brighton	
Sussex	
BN1 8YA	Tel: 01273 553243

Set next door to the bakery, in the village street of the old Patcham village and owned by proprietor Mrs Harriet Hawley, The Coach House Tearooms are near to the longest tythe barn in Sussex. They are opposite what is thought to be one of the oldest dove cotes in existence, which has walls three feet thick and 550 nesting holes.

The traditional coach house has high wooden entrance doors, flint walls and a gallery, and is wonderfully decorated with horse harnesses and brasses. The walled patio and garden has a small pond with a fountain; in the warm summer months it is very secluded and quiet.

The menu offers a range of delicious home made food; light lunches including fresh quiche, cream teas, and treats such as strawberry meringue, chocolate meringue, fresh fruit tortes, vegetarian tartlets, carrot cake and scones. Teas available include Assam, Earl Grey, Darjeeling and a selection of fruit and herbal teas.

Hours of business:
Winter - Tuesdays to Saturdays - 10am to 4pm
Summer - Tuesdays to Saturdays - 10am to 5pm
Closed on Sundays and Mondays
Closed from Christmas Eve for 3 weeks.

Fir Tree House Tea Rooms

Penshurst   Disabled Access
Kent   Parking - within 50m
TN11 8DB   Tel: 01892 870382

The Fir Tree House Tea Rooms are set in the centre of the village, next to the village hall, and close to the vineyards in a delightful sixteenth century building with inglenook fireplace, polished floors and peaceful atmosphere. The pretty cottage garden is open in summer and has won the "Best Afternoon Tea Competition" run by the tourist authority.

A local attraction is Penshurst Place, where both the house and gardens are well worth a visit.

Traditional Afternoon Tea for just £5.20 serves scones with cream and jam, sandwiches, home made cake and a pot of tea, or for those with a smaller appetite, one may order just tea and scones for £3.00. All the food is home baked on the premises, and is complemented by a range of speciality, herbal and fruit teas.

Hours of business:
Tuesdays to Fridays - 2pm to 5.30pm
Saturdays and Sundays - 1.30pm to 6pm
Closed on Mondays
Closed from November to March.

Quaintways Tearooms
High Street   Disabled Access
Penshurst   Parking - within 50m
Tonbridge
Kent
TN11 8BT   Tel: 01892 870272

Situated in the centre of the historic village, Quaintways Tearooms, a 16th century building, is close to Penshurst Place and vineyards. With a wealth of beams, the rear tearoom is a converted bakehouse, which retains its Victorian oven. The premises are shared by an antique showroom and a gift shop where you may purchase jam, chocolates, greetings cards and antiques.

Local attractions include Penshurst Place, Hever Castle and Tunbridge Wells.

Quaintways Cream Tea consists of two home made scones with butter, cream and jam, with a choice of tea or coffee for £2.90. Cakes and scones are home baked with home made tea breads and local untreated cream.

There is a large selection of fruit and herbal teas as well as the ever popular Assam, Ceylon, China, Darjeeling and Earl Grey.

Hours of business:
Summer - daily - 10am to 5.30pm.
Winter - daily - 10am to 5pm

The Old Cartlodge Tearooms
Dunley Hill   Disabled Access
Ranmore   Parking - on premises
Dorking
Surrey
RH5 6SX   Tel: 01483 282222

Close to several National Trust properties, and Denbies', the largest vineyard in England, The Old Cartlodge Tearooms are set off the road, on a working farm in the middle of the North Downs. It is easily accessible from the North Downs Way.

The two hundred year old building, made of flint, has been converted from farm use and has a small garden to enjoy when the weather permits. Inside, the exposed beams, wood fire and pine furniture all contribute to give these tearooms a rustic charm.

There is no set tea menu, allowing guests to have as much or as little as they wish, and to pick and choose from a selection of over thirty home made cakes. Some unusual specialities, such as parsnip cake, red wine and chocolate cake, or chocolate and courgette cake are well worth tasting! Local Surrey produce is used whenever possible in the mouthwatering menu of home cooked foods, that is changed each week.

Hours of business:
Open Tuesdays to Sundays.-
February - 10am to 4pm
March & April - 10am to 4.30pm
May until October - 10am to 5pm
November & December - 10am to 4.30pm
December - 10am to 4pm
Closed mid December to February.

Cobweb Tea Rooms
49 The Hundred
Romsey   Parking - within 100m
Hampshire
SO51 8GE   Tel: 01794 516434

Cobweb Tea Rooms, within easy access of Romsey Abbey, is a Georgian property with hanging baskets, oak beams and a delightful enclosed patio garden in the summer. Very courteous waitress service and a No Smoking Policy make a pleasant atmosphere. A toy box makes children welcome. In the area, local attractions include Broadlands, Romsey Abbey, King Johns House, Hilliers Arboretum and Mottisfont Abbey.

On beautifully laid out tables, Cobweb Cream Tea is served, consisting of two home made scones, with jam, cream and tea. There is a scrumptious selection of home baked cakes and pastries on display; too good to miss!

Child size portions and feeding cups can be provided. As well as various herbal teas, there is Assam, Ceylon, China, Darjeeling and Earl Grey.

Hours of business:
Tuesdays to Saturdays - 10am to 5.30pm
Closed on Sundays and Mondays.
Closed for two weeks over Christmas and New Year.

Little Cottage Tearooms

The Quay   Disabled Access
Sandwich   Parking - within 50m
Kent
CT13 9EN   Tel: 01304 614387

In the medieval market town of Sandwich, with its Roman Fort and numerous antique shops, Little Cottage Tearooms can be found opposite the River Stour on the quay by the Barbican. The three hundred year old cottage has walls two feet thick, decorated in pale pink, and tables with pink tablecloths and lace covers. In summer tables are available outside.

Smoking is allowed upstairs only, apart from Sundays. Proprietors Sue and Phil Wendholt hold three Clean Food Awards and the Healthy Heart Award.

Tea consists of a sandwich of your choice followed by a scone with butter, jam and cream plus a home made cake, and a pot of tea or coffee, all for £3.60. As well as the traditional afternoon teas, full breakfasts and lunches are offered, the specialities of the house being Buck Rarebits, chicken and mushroom pie and traditional Sunday lunch with at least seven fresh vegetables.

Hours of business:
Daily - 10am to 5pm.
Closed Mondays and Fridays except Bank Holidays.

Dunnose Cottage Tea Rooms
Luccombe Chine   Disabled Access
Nr Shanklin   Parking - within 50m
Isle of Wight
PO37 6RH   Tel: 01983 862585

Nestling in a secluded valley on National Trust land, Dunnose Cottage is set in three and a half acres of its own award winning gardens, and can be found just off the coastal road mid-way between Shanklin Old Town and Ventnor.

The gardens specialise in herbaceous borders and roses; the thatched cottage itself is sixteenth century Grade II listed and is newly refurbished. For summer afternoon tea, the superb terrace provides the ideal place to relax and enjoy the high quality produce of Dunnose Cottage Tea Rooms.

Amongst the many items on an extensive menu that includes breakfasts, lunches, main courses and afternoon teas, the Cream Teas are temptingly priced at £3.50, or £2.15 for a Half Cream Tea; ideal for those with smaller appetites! In addition to the traditional tea room items, perhaps a Strawberry Special of strawberries, clotted cream and ice cream, walnut and ginger teabread, or a visit to the superbly stocked patisserie cabinet may tempt you!

In balance with the menu, an extensive range of teas, coffees and cold drinks are available.

Hours of business:
Mondays to Sundays - 10am to 5pm.

Luccombe Tea Gardens
Luccombe Cliff
Shanklin   Parking - on premises
Isle of Wight
PO37 6RH   Tel: 01983 863116

Close to Shanklin Old Village, along the beautiful cliff top walk to Ventnor, Luccombe Tea Gardens enjoy a spectacular location where peace and clean air reign. Established in 1920, these tea gardens are set in a peaceful idyllic location offering sea and woodland views well away from the roads and traffic.

Seating is mainly outside, being very much a tea garden. This venue is generally more suited to walkers than car drivers, although limited parking is available on the premises for the elderly or infirm. Alternatively, the nearest on road parking is approximately quarter of a mile away from the Tea Gardens.

Cream Tea offers the hungry walker a delicious home made scone with jam, clotted cream and a pot of tea for £1.95. There is no set menu otherwise but a selection of morning coffees, light lunches, snacks, ice creams and home made cakes are available each day. Teas to wash it all down include Ceylon and Earl Grey.

Hours of business:
1 April to 31 October - open daily 10am to 6pm
1 November to 31 March - open weekends 10.30am to 3.30pm.

The Old Thatch Tea Shop
4 Church Road
Old Village   Parking - within 50m
Shanklin
Isle of Wight
PO37 6NU   Tel: 01983 863184

Situated in the heart of the old village, close to the Crab Inn and Chine entrance, The Old Thatch Tea Shop is one of the group of thatched buildings which formed the centre of early Shanklin. The Old Thatch is thought to be more than three hundred years old and in 1846 became Shanklin's first post office. It was also a circulating library and bookshop.

Late in the 1800s, Old Thatch became a private residence until its conversion to a tea shop in 1940. The picturesque cottage has a pretty tea garden which is used in the summer months. The proprietors, Lesley and Trevor give a warm welcome and sincerely hope you enjoy your visit.

The Old Thatch Cream Tea comprises two home made scones, butter, strawberry preserve and farmhouse clotted cream. Cakes are all home made as is the day's soup. The fresh local crab sandwich makes a tempting delicacy. Food can be complemented by a cup of Earl Grey or a herbal tea, or a refreshing glass of Elderflower Presse. Delicious!

Hours of business:
From 1st February to 30th November - open daily 10am to 5pm.

The Pantry
1A The Pantiles
Ferringham Lane
South Ferring
West Sussex
BN12 5NE

Disabled Access
Parking - on premises

Tel: 01903 503957

Set in a picturesque village by the sea, the tea room provides a setting for Sussex crafts and paintings. Although only small, it is cosy, with old fashioned gate-leg tables complementing the traditional style of the tea room. The various sizes and colours of the china teapots often provoke favourable comment.

Located around the corner from Beresford Stores and post office, The Pantry is surrounded by local attractions such as Little Paddocks Pond, the seafront at South Ferring, Highdown Gardens and the Sistine Chapel Ceiling Replica at English Martyrs Church, Goring by Sea.

The Pantry Clotted Cream Tea comprises a pot of tea with two home made scones, butter, jam and clotted cream. And home made is the order of the day here, with home made cakes, scones, desserts, ice cream, preserves and fresh cream meringues. The teas available include Indian, Earl Grey and herbal.

Hours of business:
Mondays to Saturdays - 9am to 5pm.
Closed on Wednesdays, Sundays and Bank Holidays.

Chapter House Refectory

St Albans Abbey   Disabled Access
Sumpter Yard   Parking - within 100m
St Albans
Hertfordshire
AL1 1BY   Tel: 01727 864208

Adjacent to the Cathedral on the ground floor of the Chapter House, the Refectory is a purpose built room in a modern Chapter House attached to the historic Abbey (founded 793 AD, rebuilt 1077AD) and Cathedral Church. The light and airy room has modern, attractive architectural features.

The food is freshly made each day, using good ingredients and there is no set menu, allowing customers to choose their favourites. A scone with butter and jam or selection of cakes are well priced, with Bakewell tart a speciality. Teas available include Assam, Ceylon, Darjeeling and Earl Grey.

Hours of business:
Open all year round
Mondays to Saturdays - 10.30am to 4.30pm
Sundays - 2.30 to 5pm.

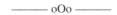

A hardened and shameless tea-drinker, who has for twenty years diluted his meals with only the infusion of this fascinating plant, whose kettle has scarcely time to cool; who with tea amuses the evening, with tea solaces the midnight and with tea welcomes the morning.

(Samuel Johnson - Review in the Literary Magazine, 1757)

Redbournbury Mill
Redbourn Road
St Albans   Parking - on premises
Hertfordshire
AL3 6RS   Tel: 01582 792874

Close to the historic Roman town of St Albans, these tea rooms occupy the first floor of a working 18th century watermill. The delightful historic building inhabits a lovely countryside setting near to the River Ver, offering some peaceful walks. Redbournbury Mill prides itself on the personal service offered to guests.

Easily located in Redbournbury Lane, which is off the A5183 St Albans to Redbourn road, there is plenty of free parking on site.

The flour used for the bread and cakes is home milled and the locally produced honey is delicious. Cream Tea offers two home made scones, jam, cream, and a pot of tea for £2.75. Guests can also choose from a menu of light refreshments and home made cakes.

Hours of business:
Open Sunday afternoons - 2.30 to 5.30pm and Bank Holidays 10am to 5pm.

——— oOo ———

Salsify (Mock Oyster) Sandwiches

Put the roots of 3 salsify into cold water, with a wine glass of vinegar and salt. Leave for an hour, then boil until tender and mash with a pint of cream. Add 2 teaspoons of anchovy sauce and cayenne pepper to taste.

(Five O'Clock Tea, 1886)

151

The Waffle House

Kingsbury Watermill   Disabled Access
St Michaels Street   Parking - on premises
St Albans
Hertfordshire
AL3 4SJ   Tel: 01727 853502

Set by the beautiful River Ver in an old watermill that dates back to Elizabethan times, The Waffle House is half a mile from the Cathedral, and close to the Roman remains. The mill itself is now a museum, having been in use for the milling of flour until 1936 and then being restored in 1973. It still retains the atmosphere of a bustling workplace and also the working machinery of the original corn crushing mill.

In season there is ample seating outside, next to the picturesque stream. Inside there is also a small shop selling pottery and gifts.

The speciality, freshly baked to order, is light and crispy Belgian style wholewheat or plain waffles. The most popular for afternoon tea is Spiced Fruit, where spice covered currants and raisins are baked into the waffle and sprinkled with cinnamon sugar. Also available are pecan and butterscotch, coconut and plain, with a variety of toppings such as maple syrup or honey, and for a little extra can be enjoyed with ice cream or fresh cream.

Along with the old favourites, Ceylon, Darjeeling and Earl Grey, there are herbal teas, filtered coffees and chilled drinks.

Hours of business:
Mondays to Saturdays - 11am to 6pm
Sundays - 12 noon to 6pm
Winter closing time is 5pm.

Oak Tree Farm Tearooms
Lymbridge Green   Disabled Access
Stowting   Parking - on premises
Nr Ashford
Kent
TN25 6BL   Tel: 01233 750297

Set in a secluded area close to Lyminge Forest, with breathtaking views of the countryside, Oak Tree Farm Tearooms is an attractive venue offering a varied menu of traditional farmhouse foods. It is especially appropriate as a stop on one of the walks through the local forests or on the Country Blossom Tours route.

In season, customers use the garden with its patio, enjoying the sumptuous fare on offer. Guests can choose between Cream Tea, Welsh Tea or Farmhouse Tea.

All baking is done on the premises, with lemon meringue pie, apple crumble pie and pavlovas amongst the available delights. There are also special salads with fruit, and on Sundays there are roast lunches.

Hours of business:
March - Sundays 12 to 5pm.
April to September incl. Tuesday to Sundays 12 to 5pm
October to January incl. Sundays 12 to 5pm.

Beam Ends Country Tea Room
Hedgers Hill
Walberton   Parking - on premises
Arundel
West Sussex
BN18 0LR   Tel: 01243 551254

Close to Arundel, Climping Beach and Binsted Woods, Beam Ends Country Tea Room is a good place to stop for a rest. The sixteenth century thatched cottage is set in one acre of wooded garden, with fine views over the valley, and a tea garden for the warmer weather.

Inside, the thirties style tea room indulges its visitors with linen tablecloths, fresh flowers, old fashioned crockery and an open fire in the winter months.

The morning coffee, lunches and afternoon teas are all prepared from fresh ingredients in their own kitchen. Cream Tea comprises two home made scones with butter, jam, cream and a pot of tea. Sandwich Tea offers a round of sandwiches, cake and a pot of tea. Cakes and scones are home made, and the tea served is made from loose leaf tea.

Hours of business:
May to September - Tuesdays to Sundays 11am to 5.30pm.
Reduced opening at other times - please call to check.

Annie's Tea Rooms
79 High Street   Disabled Access
Wallingford   Parking - within 50m
Oxfordshire
OX10 0BX   Tel: 01491 836308

Not far from the castle gardens and the river, this seventeenth century building has a clean, healthy environment, with a No Smoking policy throughout. The décor is attractive, the atmosphere peaceful and there is a friendly and courteous waitress service. A small walled garden with seating provides a secluded spot for afternoon tea in the summer months.

The wonderful range of set teas on the menu include Cake Tea, Cottage Tea, Afternoon Tea, High Tea, Cream Tea and Tea Cake Tea. High Tea presents a pot of tea with two slices of bread and butter, home made jam and two cakes. Cakes, scones, jams and teacakes are all home baked, and an incredible variety of approximately thirty different cakes is available; the home made teacakes being particularly popular.

Teas include Assam, Ceylon, Darjeeling, Earl Grey, Lapsang Souchong, Lemon, Jasmine, Blackcurrant and Traditional English.

Hours of business:
October to June - Mondays to Saturdays 10am to 5pm (closed Wednesdays and Sundays).
July to September - Mondays to Saturdays 10am to 5.30pm, Sundays 2.30pm to 5.30pm (closed on Wednesdays).

Lainston House Hotel & Restaurant

Sparsholt	Disabled Access
Winchester	Parking - on premises
Hampshire	
SO21 2LT	Tel: 01962 863588

Lainston House Hotel is situated two miles outside Winchester on the B3049 Stockbridge Road, well signposted on the left. Local attractions include Winchester Cathedral and College, and King Arthur's Round Table in the historic City of Winchester, the ancient capital of England. Nearby are the Rivers Test and Itchen, Marwell Zoological Park and the Watercress Line Railway at Alresford.

At Lainston House, the Drawing Room and Cedar Bar are delightful settings within the William and Mary Period House. From both rooms, views overlooking the Hampshire countryside can be enjoyed. Tea is also served on the South Lawn and Front Terrace which again incorporate the fabulous view. Tea is served on the finest white china and refined with silver condiments and cutlery, all dressed with distinguished Swiss table linen.

All the pastries and cakes are made and baked daily by their extremely talented brigade of chefs, and in particular, the home made scones are a must to try. Truly wonderful! To cater for any individual's needs, all teas can be offered from Earl Grey to Rosehip and Peppermint.

The Lainston House Cream Tea consists of warm scones, served with strawberry preserve and clotted cream, fruit cake, marble cake, fruit tartlets and eclairs, together with a choice of tea for £8.00. Cakes can be boxed to take home, should you be unable to consume them all!

Hours of business:
Open 24 hours a day, seven days a week.
Booking advised for afternoon tea.

Jennie Wren's Tea Rooms

23 Market Square   Disabled Access
Winslow   Parking - within 50m
Buckinghamshire
MK18 3AB   Tel: 01296 715499

Housed in a listed building in the main market square, Jennie Wren's Tea Rooms are close to Winslow Hall, reputed to have been built by Christopher Wren. Local attractions include Winslow Hall, Keach's Chapel and Claydon House.

The proprietor, Jennifer Nilsen, welcomes guests to wood panelled rooms with tables that are actually old treadle sewing machines bases, covered with hand embroidered tablecloths. Concessions to twentieth century life include solar panels for hot water and winning the W.I. Best Ladies Loo in Buckinghamshire award, 1994, and the Roy Castle Good Air Award for being completely non smoking.

There is a private dining room available for up to sixteen people and disabled access is at the rear of the building.

Afternoon Tea comprises assorted sandwiches, scone, cream, homemade preserve, a pot of tea or coffee and is competitively priced. Farmhouse Tea substitutes two fried eggs on toast for the sandwiches. Assam, Ceylon, China, Earl Grey and Darjeeling teas are available. All day breakfasts, salads, jacket potatoes and home made cakes all feature on the menu.

Hours of business:
Tuesdays to Saturdays - 9.30am to 5pm
Sundays - 11am to 5pm.

South West

The Old Schoolhouse
1 Back Street
Abbotsbury   Parking   within 50m
Dorset
DT3 4JP   Tel: 01305 871808

The Old Schoolhouse Tea Rooms are in the centre of the village, famous for its swannery. Other local sights include the Tythe Barn and childrens farm, sub tropical gardens, St Catherines Chapel and Chesil Beach.

The décor is of the 1920s and '30s with rose and lace tablecloths, music of the era, walls crammed with old pictures, newspapers and magazine advertisements and waitresses dressed in "Nippy" style black dresses with long white aprons. Roger and Jacqui, the proprietors, welcome you to their tea room and gift shop where the service is cheerful and relaxed, and where they are proud not to provide a fast food operation! It is a no smoking establishment and children under five are not admitted.

Traditional Cream Tea for one comprises two delicious 'own made' scones with locally produced clotted cream and strawberry jam, along with a pot of tea. The Schoolhouse Complete Tea gives a choice of sandwich served with salad and potato crisps and a pot of tea followed by 'own made' cake or scone with jam and cream. The delicious 'own made' cakes include Traditional Dorset apple cake, served warm with clotted cream, rich fruit cake, made with more than a hint of Scotch whisky, plus an ever evolving range as available!

Hours of business:
All year round - daily 10.30am to 5.15pm.
Closed on Wednesdays.

The Village Shoppe & Tea Rooms
The Square
Atherington   Parking - on premises
Umberleigh
Devon
EX37 9HY   Tel: 01769 560248

The Village Shoppe and Tea Rooms is a fifteenth century building with wooden beams and inglenook fireplace, set in a pretty Devon village opposite Atherington Parish Church. The Tea Rooms have an historic ambience; even the tables are over fifty years old. Parking is available in the village square itself.

There is a choice of three set Afternoon Teas; Cream Tea, Mini Cream Tea and Devon Tea, all very reasonably priced. The Mini Cream Tea serves one scone with jam and cream, a home made cake and a pot of tea for £2.65. Home made cakes, pickles, jams and marmalades are available for purchase, and the cakes served are all home made too. A range of light lunches are available and a speciality is the Sunday lunch.

Hours of business:
Sundays - 10am to 5pm
Mondays - closed (except during August)
Tuesdays to Fridays - 9am to 5.30pm
Saturdays - 9am to 5pm.

Carpenters Kitchen
The Harbour   Disabled Access
Boscastle   Parking - within 100m
Cornwall
PL35 0HD   Tel: 01840 250595

Built in local Cornish stone, on the site of the old carpenters workshop from the days when the village was part of the Manor estate, Carpenters Kitchen is located by the side of the River Valency.

Inside, the walls are decorated with wisteria stencilling and photographs of the old workshop and the carpenters who toiled there. The wooden floors, tables and chairs add to the cosy atmosphere, rounded off in winter months with an open fire in the hearth. Walking towards the harbour, Carpenters Kitchen is on the left of the river, opposite the National Trust Information Shop.

Everything except the sliced bread is made on the premises. There is a mouthwatering selection to choose from including tea cakes, scones, rolls and Cornish splits, or for the sweeter tooth, meringues, gateaux, cheesecakes and specialities including meringue specials with Carte D'Or Ice Cream or traditional Cornish Dairy Ice Cream.

The menu, including Cream Tea, is offered throughout the day, and in summer, seating is popular outside on the forecourt. The proprietors, Debbie and Geoff Beszant, are founder members of the Guild of Tea Shops in Cornwall.

Hours of business:
April to October - daily - 10.30am to 5.30pm
November & March - weekends only - 10.30am to 5pm
December 27th - 1st January inc. 10.30am to 5pm.

The Old Cottage Tea Shop
20 Fore Street   Disabled Access
Bovey Tracey
Newton Abbot
Devon
TQ13 9AD   Tel: 01626 833430

The Old Cottage Tea Shop was established during the 1950's. A traditional olde worlde cottage situated at the lower end of Main Street, the interior features beams and a Devon stone fireplace. The teashop has been a winner of Britain in Bloom for its beautiful window boxes and hanging baskets.

Devon Cream Tea provides two delicious scones, jam and clotted cream and a pot of tea for £2.90. Afternoon Tea offers a choice of sandwiches, a scone with jam and clotted cream and a choice of home made cake and a pot of tea for £3.75.

There are a wide range of scones and these, along with cakes and jam, are all home made, using fresh local ingredients. Other specialities include fruit pies and mousses, clotted cream meringues and locally made ice cream. A new speciality for this summer will be the locally made pasties, including a vegetarian option, and pâtés. Among the teas are Assam, Ceylon, China, Darjeeling and Earl Grey.

Hours of business:
Daily 10am to 5.30pm
Except Wednesdays - 10am to 2pm and closed on Sundays.

Pink's Place
Courtenay House
76 Fore Street   Parking - within 50m
Bovey Tracey
Devon
TQ13 9AE   Tel: 01626 835363

Mentioned in the Bovey Guide, Courtenay House has an historical
background. Built in 1876, it was known as the "mission house" as it was
run by nuns who looked after 'wayward' girls. It is close to the natural
beauty of Dartmoor and Becky Falls, and the attractions of Bovey Mill and
the Guild of Devon Crafts.

With gardens front and back, the proprietor, Tina Richardson, has created
a homely atmosphere full of period charm, with old tableware and linen
tablecloths with lace and embroidery, antiques and bric-a-brac.

Cream Tea comprises two scones (fruit or plain) with jams and clotted
cream from the farm, along with a choice of tea or coffee. Afternoon Tea
adds a choice of sandwich and a slice of cake. All desserts and cakes are
made by the proprietor, and among the teas are a choice of Assam, China,
Darjeeling and Earl Grey.

Hours of business:
Open seven days a week - Mondays to Fridays 9am to 7pm
Saturdays and Sundays 9am to 5.30pm
Open Christmas Day and Boxing Day.

Wind in the Willows Tea Garden

Riverway   Disabled Access
Charmouth   Parking - within 100m
Dorset
DT6 6LS   Tel: 01297 560384

Walking towards East Beach at Charmouth, a cutout plywood Toad points the way to the Wind in the Willows Tea Garden. Cars should be parked at the Beach Car Park, and the short distance covered on foot, as there is no car parking in Riverway.

In the area, the Jurassic coastline and beaches offer fossils to those who search, and it is excellent walking country.

The secluded tea garden has a sense of tranquillity and escapism about it, with the theme of the Wind in the Willows appearing in the menu.

The phrase "delicious fresh cream teas with all the trimmings - all summer long" is a very fitting description of the afternoon teas at this venue. Children, dogs, in fact, everybody, is welcome.

The 'delicious fresh cream tea' serves two scones, plenty of clotted cream, strawberry jam and a pot of tea for just £3.00. Cake of the day is available, as are locally made biscuits, and for warmer days, ginger beer or orange cordial are waiting to quench the thirst.

Hours of business:
Open afternoons daily 2pm to 6pm.
Closed 1st October to end of May. Reopens Whit week.

Hillside Cottage Tearooms
The Cliffs
Cheddar   Parking - within 100m
Somerset
BS27 3QH   Tel: 01934 743158

Situated between Gough's and Cox's Caves on the opposite side of the road, overlooking a large picturesque lake, the tearooms are set in about a third of an acre of terraced garden. The two hundred year old cottage was re-established as a tearoom in 1984, having been a tearoom around the turn of the century. Behind towers the massive bulk of Lion Rock.

Local attractions include the famous Cheddar showcaves, the Mendip Hills and Cheddar Gorge Cheese Company, and of course, the rural village of Cheddar itself.

Cream Tea serves two sultana scones, Somerset clotted cream and jam with a pot of tea for one for just £2.50. Cakes and scones are home baked, with apple pie, sultana flapjack, cherry shortcake and farmhouse fruitcake all tempting the hungry customer.

There is also an extensive range of Marshfield Farm real dairy ice cream sundaes. Teas include Assam, Darjeeling and Earl Grey and a range of herbal teas.

Hours of business:
Daily - 10.30am to 5pm (open until 6pm in summer season).
May be closed in December and January.

Court Barn Hotel

Clawton   Disabled Access
Holsworthy   Parking - on premises
Devon
EX22 6PS   Tel: 01409 271219

Standing next to Clawton's twelfth century church, half a mile from the A388, the Court Barn Hotel is an ideal centre from which to enjoy Devon. Locally the Roadford Lakes, Atlantic Heritage Coast and Holsworthy market are all worth a visit.

The building was rebuilt in 1853 from a sixteenth century manor house and stands in five acres of parkland. The house is full of antiques, paintings and objets d'art. Tea can be taken in the restaurant, one of the lounges, which have crackling log fires in the winter, or outside during the summer months. A member of the Guild of Tea Shops, it is also Egon Ronay recommended.

The menu abounds with mouthwatering home made delights; ice creams, cakes, jams, meringues and other delicious desserts. The marsala and almond, honey and cherry, and chocolate and walnut cakes are top of the list to try. The Court Barn Special Tea comprises a pot of tea, cucumber sandwiches, choice of cakes followed by home made meringues with clotted cream all for £5.50.

The proprietors, Robert and Susan Wood round off an excellent menu with the availability of 45 different teas, including speciality, exotic, and herbal. A real treat!

Hours of business:
Open every day except 2nd to 12th January.

The White Cottage

Dolphin Street   Disabled Access
Colyton   Parking - on premises
Devon
EX13 6NA   Tel: 01297 552401

The White Cottage, a Grade II Listed building, is a fifteenth century Hotel and Tea Gardens operated by its resident proprietors, Lawreece and Ann Parker. It is situated approximately 250 metres down hill from the Market Square.

The unique medieval town with its circular narrow street pattern was officially decreed a town under a Royal Charter of 1546. There is also a fifteenth century Church with Lantern Tower.

Speciality products include West Country Cream Teas, treacle tart and bread and butter Pudding, and there is a special children's tea menu. Devonshire Cream Tea serves two home made scones, a bowl of jam, a bowl of cream and a pot of tea for just £3.45 per person.

All cakes and scones are home made on the premises, including the mouthwatering lemon spicey cake and shortbread, and a variety of teas, including herb teas, are available.

Hours of business:
Daily from 9.30am to 6pm
Telephone to check during winter season

The Flemish Weaver Tea Rooms
55 High Street   Disabled Access
Corsham   Parking - within 50m
Wiltshire
SN13 0EZ   Tel: 01249 714931

The Flemish Weaver Tea Rooms can be found in the High Street in Corsham, close to the post office and Town Hall. Within the area, places to visit include Corsham Court, the historic city of Bath, Lacock and Castle Combe. Corsham is situated just off the A4 between Chippenham and Bath.

The delightful Edwardian building is beautifully decorated to a high standard and features the works of local artists. During the warmer summer months, dining at tables outside on the pavement is popular.

The Tea Rooms provide a full lunch menu, Afternoon Teas and Cream Teas. All the products are made on the premises using fresh local produce, including local honey.

A full Clotted Cream Tea with delicious home made scones and jam is available for just £3.75 including your choice of tea or coffee. Or for £3.25, why not try the Edwardian Tea with cake? Speciality teas are on the menu, as are specially imported coffee beans, freshly ground on the premises. Freshly ground coffee is also available for sale. An aromatic memento of your visit to The Flemish Weaver Tea Rooms.

Hours of business:
Mondays to Saturdays - 9am - 5pm.

Crumms

Unit 9 George Centre   Disabled Access
Crewkerne   Parking - within 50m
Somerset
TA18 7LU   Tel: 01460 76965

Crumms is located by the car park in a quiet, pretty shopping arcade. The small eatery is clean with reasonable prices and the option of eating al fresco, weather permitting. In the locality, places of interest include the Church and the antique shops, particularly Lawrences Auction Rooms.

The speciality here are the sandwiches, which can be served on the premises, or prepared for you to take away. The selection is extensive and innovative. The menu includes home made soups, light lunches, home baked cakes and a range of teas and coffees.

Hours of business:
Mondays to Fridays - 8.30am to 5pm
Saturdays - 9.30am to 5pm
Closed Sundays.

——— oOo ———

Tea, though ridiculed by those who are naturally coarse in their nervous sensibilities..... will always be the favourite beverage of the intellectual.

(Thomas de Quincy - Confessions of an English Opium Eater)

The Old Tea House
44 High West Street
Dorchester   Disabled Access
Dorset   Parking - within 50m
DT1 1UT
                                              Tel: 01305 263719

The Old Tea House can be found at the top end of the town, close to the museums and the Roman Town House. Built in 1635, it was originally an abbot's dwelling. The inglenook fireplace, exposed beams and gas lamps give an historic ambience. A secluded old English walled garden is used for outside dining when the weather permits.

In the locality, there is much to see including the Military Museum, Dorset Museum, the Court House, the Roman Town House and the Dinosaur Museum, as well as the beautiful town of Dorchester itself.

Dorset Cream Teas offer two home made scones, jam, clotted cream and a pot of tea for £3.40. The cakes, scones, soups and dish of the day are all home made. Dorset Apple Cake is a speciality which must be tasted! A good selection of speciality teas is available, in addition to a range of other hot and cold drinks to suit all tastes.

Hours of business:
Tuesdays to Sundays - 10am to 5pm
Closed on Mondays except for Bank Holidays.

Crumbs
38 Fore Street
Fowey   Parking - within 50m
Cornwall
PL23 1AQ   Tel: 01726 833603

Next to the main Post Office in Fowey, Crumbs is in a prime spot for various coastal walks and near to the beautiful, historic harbour which offers sailing and yachting. An artist works on the premises and the area is shared with an art gallery and gift shop, selling original art and prints, greetings cards and music.

Cream Tea offers a pot of tea, two scones (plain or fruit), strawberry jam and clotted cream. Most food is made on the premises and there is local farmhouse ice cream. Home made pasties and a range of home baked scones, filled French sticks and fresh local crab are available to tempt the hungry visitor. Teas include Assam, Darjeeling, Earl Grey and various herbal infusions.

Hours of business:
Mondays to Saturdays - 10am to 5pm.
Sundays - 12 to 5pm
Reduced opening hours from November to February.

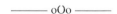

Thunder and Lightning Sandwiches
Spread the bread with golden syrup and cover with Devon cream.

(Five O'Clock Tea, 1886)

Fairwater Head Hotel

Hawkchurch   Disabled Access
Axminster   Parking - on premises
Devon
EX13 5TX   Tel: 01297 678349

Established in the 1960s, the Fairwater Head Hotel is signposted off the B3165 Lyme Regis to Crewkerne Road. Hawkchurch is known as the "village of roses" and the beautifully landscaped gardens of the hotel have won the Ashley catering award for being one of the "Best Ten Hotel Gardens".

The Edwardian country house has panoramic views over the Axe Valley, and these views can be enjoyed from the lounges where in winter months the log fires burn brightly.

Rather than a set menu, The Fairwater Head Hotel offers a choice of home baked cream cakes, fruit cakes, biscuits and scones with local cream and preserve. Scones, clotted cream and preserve come reasonably priced at £3.00 a head, with a good selection of teas to quench your thirst.

Hours of business:
Open daily.
Closed from December to February.

Trevarno Estate & Gardens

Trevarno Manor   Disabled Access
Helston   Parking - on premises
Cornwall
TR13 0RU   Tel: 01362 574274

Signed from the B3302 junction with the Helston to Penzance road, this conservatory Tea Room has a central fountain feature. The tables and seating are arranged between beds planted with aromatic plants and Lemon Trees being another particular feature.

The view from the conservatory is to the Camellia garden across a lawn where peacocks and pheasants roam freely. There is only partial disabled access at the present time.

Cornish Ice Cream is a speciality of the tea rooms and, along with the home made cakes, baked on the premises, there is a range of herbal and fruit teas. The menu, which includes soups and jacket potatoes, is in the process of being extended to introduce a wide variety of teas, coffees and soft drinks.

Cream Tea consisting of two scones, strawberry jam, Cornish clotted cream and a pot of tea is a reasonable £2.50, and the selection of mouthwatering cakes include Granny's apple cake, Trevarno chocolate cake, Siubhan's chocolate muffin and old fashioned ginger cake. Last food orders are taken at 4.30pm.

Hours of business:
Open every day, except Christmas Day, from 10.30am to 5pm.

The Horner Tea Gardens

Horner   Disabled Access
Nr Minehead   Parking - within 50m
Somerset
TA24 8HY   Tel: 01643 862380

Situated on Exmoor and not far from Dunkery Beacon and Horner Water which offer walks and horse riding, the Horner Tea Gardens enjoy panoramic scenic views of the surrounding countryside. The Grade II listed building stands in a small, quiet hamlet with a water mill nearby and wooded walks available, and welcomes dogs and can cater for parties.

Cream Tea consists of tea, scones, clotted cream and jam. Alternatively, there is a Special Cream Tea which includes cakes as well as the above. Cakes and scones are home baked and the range of desserts is very tempting, including mississippi mud pie, rocky chocky peanut dream and caramel toffee cheesecake, all served with your choice of clotted cream or ice cream. Mouthwatering! Tea, herb tea, and a range of coffees are also on offer.

Light lunches are served from 12 noon until 2pm, featuring pizzas, salads, omelettes and ploughmans.

Hours of business:
Daily - 11am to 6pm in July and August.
Daily - 11am to 5.30pm during rest of the year.
Closed from November to March.

Mad Hatter's Teashop

28 Church Street   Disabled Access

Launceston   Parking - within 50m

Cornwall

PL15 8AR   Tel: 01566 777188

The Mad Hatter's Teashop - "the teashop full of surprises" - is about 50 metres from the town square and opposite WH Smith. The local area provides such attractions as Launceston Castle, Steam Railway, and the Otter Sanctuary. Mad Hatter's is a non smoking establishment.

Lewis Carroll's characters are everywhere - on the walls, in the menu - and the Mad Hatter is even there in person every Saturday and holiday! All teas and children's drinks are served in novelty tea pots and a wide selection of tea pots are also available for sale. Mad Hatter's has been a finalist in the Top Tea Place of the Year Award '96 and '97, and been awarded the Heartbeat Award.

The menu is as innovative as the atmosphere, with Mad Hatter's Platters (ploughmans), Alice's Scrumptious Sandwiches (such as avocado with mint and coriander), March Hare's Marvellous Cakes, Mad Hatter's Specials (Afternoon teas) and the Dormouse Selection (the healthier options). Being spoilt for choice, don't miss The Indecisive Cake Taster which allows you to sample three pieces of cake or gateau for just £2.25. House tea, speciality teas, scented teas, herbal teas and an excellent range of coffees are available, including choices for the children. Whether adult or child, this is a place to have fun, and enjoy some delicious food too!

Hours of business:

Mondays to Saturdays 10am to 5.30pm

Sundays (in summer only) and Bank Holidays 11am to 4.30pm

Times may vary - please telephone to confirm.

Fuchsia Tea Room

Fuchsia Valley   Disabled Access
Lee   Parking - within 50m
Nr Ilfracombe
Devon
EX34 8LW   Tel: 01271 863551

Located opposite "Old Maid's Cottage" in the village centre, Fuchsia Tea Room is close to Sandy Beach and many lovely walks in a Heritage Coast area with fuchsias in profusion. Set in a steep sided, wooded valley, a small bridge over a stream leads to the tea room and shop.

Fuchsias are the theme of the décor of the tea room and plants are available for sale; in keeping, the tea garden is fronted by a fuchsia hedge. This has been the site of a tea room since approximately 1930.

Clotted Cream Tea offers two home made scones, jam, cream and a pot of tea or coffee for just £2.65. For the walker with an appetite, the Afternoon Tea offers a sandwich, a slice of home made cake, a scone with jam and cream and a pot of tea or coffee. You will find it hard to resist the clotted cream fudge on sale, an ideal gift to take home. Also available are ice creams, toasties, light lunches and food to take away. Don't forget to purchase a fuchsia plant as a memento on your way out!

Hours of business:
Sundays to Fridays - 10.30am to 5pm.
Saturdays - 3pm to 5pm.
Closed after October half term until Mothers Day in March.

Primrose Cottage

Lustleigh   Disabled Access
Newton Abbot   Parking - within 50m
Devon
TQ13 9TB   Tel: 01647 277365

Set opposite the old church in the village of Lustleigh within Dartmoor National Park and with lovely walks and bridle paths nearby, Primrose Cottage, dating from the fifteenth century, has a thatched roof and pretty gardens overlooking the river. Lustleigh is located off the A382 Bovey to Moretonhampstead road. Local attractions include the bird watching and walking on scenic Dartmoor.

Inside, the décor is cosy with charming crockery and a tempting display of cakes in the cabinet. The atmosphere is pleasant and relaxed, definitely a place to linger! Customers return time and time again to enjoy the food and ambience here.

Alongside a menu offering delicious light lunches all day, guests may choose from Cream Tea or Cheese Tea as set menus, or combine items for an individual afternoon tea. Cream Tea serves two home made scones (wholemeal, plain or fruit), two jams, clotted cream and a pot of tea or coffee. Cheese Tea offers Stilton or Cheddar cheese instead of the jams. This makes a refreshing change.

Home made cakes, such as gateaux, pavlovas, meringues, cheesecakes and roulades are too tempting to miss, and delicious lunches are also on the menu.

Hours of business:
Open daily, except Tuesdays from 10.30am to 5.30pm.
Sundays and Bank Holidays from 10.30am to 6.30pm.
Closed from end of November to end of February.

Gilly's Tearoom
Market Place
Marazion   Parking - within 50m
Penzance
Cornwall
TR17 0AR   Tel: 01736 710327

The tea room is in the centre of Marazion, opposite All Saints' Church, with easy access to St Michael's Mount and is recommended in the Good Cream Tea Guide. Nearby Marazion Marsh is a haven for birdwatching visitors.

Inside, tablecloths and aprons complement the china ware and on sunny days it is possible to sit at the tables in front of the building where flower baskets make a pretty sight. There is a no smoking policy inside the tea room, but smoking and dogs are welcome outside.

The proprietors are the Hiscocks who aim to give value for money with fast and friendly service. Scones and cakes are all home baked, with a choice of specialities like banana cake, carrot cake and chocolate fudge cake. A variety of jams and other home cooked food are also available for you to enjoy. A range of herbal teas and old favourites Assam, Ceylon, China, Darjeeling and Earl Grey are served. And you cannot leave without trying some of the assorted flavours of Cornish ice cream and fudge that are available!

Hours of business:
Closed from end October to March.

Sail Loft Restaurant

St Michael's Mount   Disabled Access
Marazion   Parking - on mainland
Penzance
Cornwall
TR17 0HT   Tel: 01736 710748

Set on the west side of the harbour on St Michael's Mount, with parking on the mainland, the local attraction is the Castle. The Mount is joined to the mainland at Marazion by a causeway at low tide; at high tide, access is made possible by boat. The Sail Loft is a converted boat store and sail loft, with good views over the harbour and Mounts Bay. The décor is beautiful, with wooden floor and panelling, and solid granite walls.

Tea is served on unique crockery featuring the family crest of the St Aubyns who live at the Castle. The fare is home made, prepared and cooked on the premises, using Cornish produce and supplies. Hot and cold food, freshly prepared filled rolls, and hot and cold drinks are on the menu.

Cornish Cream Tea consists of a pot of National Trust tea with home made splits or scones, strawberry preserve or honey, and Cornish clotted cream. Also available is the local Cornish dairy ice cream, as well as a range of home baked bread, cakes and biscuits using locally produced ingredients. Teas available include Earl Grey, Darjeeling and Assam

Hours of business:
1st April to 31st October - daily 10.30am to 5.30pm (closing time 4.30pm in March, April and October).
Hours variable according to weather and tides.

Rectory Farm Tea Rooms

Rectory Farm   Disabled Access
Crosstown   Parking - on premises
Morwenstow
Nr Bude
Cornwall
EX23 9SR   Tel: 01288 331251

Situated opposite the ancient Church of John the Baptist, Rectory Farm
Tea Rooms are only five hundred yards from some of the most spectacular
cliffs of North Cornwall, with a coastal footpath leading to a cliff walk.
This is a working farm that has been in the same family for over fifty
years.

The farmhouse dates from 1296 when it was owned by the Monks of St
John of Bridgwater, and the tea rooms themselves are located in what used
to be the Main Hall which has ancient flagstone floors, two huge open
fireplaces, beamed ceilings and is wonderfully furnished with antique
furniture and chintz soft furnishings. Take in the wonderful atmosphere as
you sample the fare!

The traditional recipes used at Rectory Farm have been passed down
through generations of the family, and fresh local produce is used
whenever possible. The display of home made cakes is very tempting, with
the likes of apricot iced fruit cake, walnut tea loaf, carrot and banana to
choose from, as well as a mouth watering array of home made biscuits and
cookies! Tea serves two large home made scones, local Cornish clotted
cream, jam and a pot of tea of your choice. Among those available are
Ceylon, China and Earl Grey.

Hours of business:
Easter to October - 11am to 5.30pm approximately
Friday and Saturday evenings - open for dinner
November to Easter - phone to check opening times.

The Tea Clipper
53a The Street   Disabled Access
Milton Abbas   Parking - within 50m
Dorset
DT11 0BP   Tel: 01258 880223

Set in the main street of picturesque village, Milton Abbas, The Tea
Clipper is surrounded by thatched, whitewashed cottages. Milton Abbey,
Park Farm Museum and the Rare Breeds Centre are local attractions to the
Grade II listed building. The Tea Clipper incorporates a gift shop stocking
a large variety of items, including wooden toys, hand made jewellery and
home made preserves.

Inside, Dorset Cream Tea revives the weary traveller with a pot of tea, two
warm scones, clotted cream and strawberry jam. Bread, cakes and scones
are all home baked on the premises, and specialities include Dorset apple
cake, and treacle and Bakewell tarts. There is a wide range of teas,
featuring Assam, Ceylon, China, Darjeeling and Earl Grey.

Hours of business:
Tuesdays to Sundays - 10.30am to 5.30pm
Closed on Mondays except Bank Holidays
Closed from mid November to mid March.

——— oOo ———

We had a kettle: we let it leak:
Our not repairing it made it worse.
We haven't had any tea for a week....
The bottom is out of the Universe!

(Rudyard Kipling)

The Old Pilchard Press
Old Quay Street   Disabled Access
Mousehole   Parking - within 50m
Penzance
Cornwall
TR19 6RY   Tel: 01736 731154

Set off the quay in the old part of the traditional fishing village and near to the birds' hospital, The Old Pilchard Press was converted from an old fish store and is made from local granite, with two foot thick walls. Also, you will find the road to the coastal footpath nearby.

Cornish Cream Tea is served at round tables in china teapots, with matching water jugs and consists of two scones, jam and clotted cream with a pot of tea or coffee for just £2.90.

Specialities include large tea cakes, carrot cake and ice creams like Knickerbocker Glories. Cakes and scones are home baked and China, Darjeeling and Earl Grey tea are served along with a selection of herbal teas.

Hours of business:
Mid February to end December - daily - 10am - 5pm
July and August - daily - 10am to 8.30pm.

Strand Tea Rooms
24 New Street   Disabled Access
Barbican   Parking - within 50m
Plymouth
Devon
PL1 5RR   Tel: 01752 251900

The Strand Tea Rooms are set on the harbourside of the Barbican, close to Plymouth Hoe and the fishing port. Close by are the National Aquarium, Plymouth Dome and the Barbican Glassworks.

The beautiful original Elizabethan building has appropriate period décor inside, where there are "Tudor" tables and a flagged floor, beamed ceilings and large windows, with views over the fishing boats moored in the harbour. Separate rooms are available for smokers and non smokers.

Along with Devon Cream Tea, using clotted cream produced on a nearby farm, there is a good selection of traditional English fare such as teacakes and crumpets, and teas includes Assam, Ceylon, China, Darjeeling and Earl Grey. Cakes and scones are all home made, and include sumptuous offerings such as caramel shortbread, rich fruit cake and toffee, apple and pecan pie served with clotted cream.

Hours of business:
Mondays to Fridays - 10am to 5pm
Saturdays and Sundays - 10am to 5.30pm.

Strand Tea Rooms, Plymouth

The Plantation Cafe

The Coombes   Disabled Access
Polperro   Parking - within 100m
Cornwall
PL13 2RG   Tel: 01503 272223

Maurice and Ann Vaughan are justly proud of their tea shop, having seen
it featured on local radio, television and even in a Japanese magazine.
Located opposite the pharmacy, between the car park and the harbour, the
Café is situated close to the Polperro Heritage Museum, and the South
West Peninsula Coastal footpath.

The Victorian building with granite exterior and slate roof, continues the
Victorian theme inside, with dark beams and white walls complementing
wheelback chairs, an open fireplace with copper hood and a display of
copper and brass pots. Tea is served on a willow pattern tea service. It was
a founder member of the Guild of Tea Shops, and has won awards for its
beautiful gardens, through which a river runs.

Cornish Cream Tea comprises two home made scones, strawberry jam,
Cornish clotted cream and a pot of tea. Scones, cakes and jams are home
made and fresh strawberries are available in season. Other local
specialities include home made Cornish fruit bread, Cornish Dairy ice
cream, and locally made pasties. Teas include some wonderful fruit and
herbal varieties, such as Camomile and Lemongrass, Passionfruit and
Vanilla, and also Assam, Ceylon, China, Darjeeling and Earl Grey.

Hours of business:
Sundays to Fridays - 10.30am to 5.30pm.
Closed on Saturdays.
Closed from November to March.

Harts Teashop
112 High Street   Disabled Access
Poole   Parking - within 50m
Dorset
BH15 1DF   Tel: 01202 685419

Midway along the High Street, Poole Quay being at one end and the main shopping centre at the other, Harts Teashop attracts shoppers from the Dolphin Centre and tourists from the picturesque Poole Quay with its fishing boats. In the vicinity are Brownsea Island and several other islands to visit, and the Royal National Lifeboats Institution's head office which is open to the public.

The shop dates from the 1920s and the proprietors have tried to reflect this in the décor, with bentwood furniture. Pottery is provided by Purbeck Pottery, a local firm situated on the quay. The atmosphere is warm and friendly.

Tea comprises two fruit scones, butter, clotted or fresh cream, strawberry jam and a pot of tea for one. Harts Teashop is renowned for delicious home made cakes, pastries and meringues. The range of teas include old favourites Assam, Ceylon, Darjeeling and Earl Grey and several ground coffees are available.

Reasonably priced light lunches are served all day with Ice Cream Sundaes during the summer months.

Hours of business:
Mondays to Saturdays - 8.30am to 5.30pm
Sundays - 10am to 4.30pm.

Camellia Coffee House
High Street
Porlock   Parking - within 50m
Somerset
TA24 8PT   Tel: 01643 862266

You will find much to observe whilst taking tea at the Camellia Coffee House, particularly the centre piece, an antique Welsh dresser.

Second hand books and products of the Exmoor Producers Association, such as cakes, garden art, hampers, chocolates and greetings cards, are on sale. Well behaved dogs are welcome here.

The Coffee House is situated in the High Street, next to the pharmacy and has disabled access to the tea shop but not to the toilets. The area surrounding Porlock is beautiful, the stunning scenery of Exmoor should not be missed and Porlock Weir Harbour is worthy of a visit.

Cream Tea serves two home made scones, clotted cream and jam with a pot of tea of the customer's choice. Cakes are hand made, and sandwiches with unusual fillings such as blue cheese, pear and walnut, or chicken, or roast beef and wholegrain mustard are a regular speciality. Pots of tea, coffee or a choice of the range of speciality teas provide liquid refreshment.

Hours of business:
From April to end of September - Mondays to Fridays 12 - 5pm and Sundays 1pm to 5pm.
Open weekends all year round.

Avalon Tea Room
Echo Corner   Disabled Access
Coast Road   Parking - on premises
Porthtowan
Truro
Cornwall
TR4 8AR   Tel: 01209 890751

At the bottom of the hill and opposite Porthtowan Garage, Avalon Tea Room is close to the beautiful sandy beach, which is ideal for walking, and frequented by surfers. The sea views are wonderful, and this being a Mining Heritage Area, there are many old mine buildings within easy walking distance.

Ann and Terry Luckwell, the owners, welcome their guests with the comfortable atmosphere and friendly service, along with the wide selection of home and locally baked scones, cakes and biscuits.

Cornish Cream Tea includes two scones or Cornish splits, jam, clotted cream and a pot of tea or cup of coffee. Or try the Avalon Tea Time Special that serves a sandwich with a choice of filling, a home baked cake or bun and a pot of tea or coffee. There is a good range of speciality teas, herbal infusions and selected blends of coffee to choose from.

Hours of business:
Mondays to Wednesdays - 8.30am to 6pm
Thursdays to Saturdays - 8.30am to 9pm
Sundays - 9am to 9pm
Closed Tuesdays except in August.

Duchy House Tea Rooms

Tavistock Road   Disabled Access
Princetown   Parking - on premises
Devon
PL20 6QF   Tel: 01822 890552

Situated in the middle of Dartmoor National Park, Princetown is the highest town in England. Duchy House, of Victorian build, can be found opposite Princetown County Primary School, and commands an outstanding view of Dartmoor from the town. The Tea Rooms are situated on ground floor level, and disabled access is possible although some assistance is required.

The small, family run business offers a friendly home environment and is a no smoking haven, apart from the real fire burning in the hearth during winter months. The owners, Ernie and Hilary Trimble, make the wonderful promise to their customers "we do not serve fast food - we serve good food as fast as we can"!

The menu is varied and tempting, with exceptional cream teas, Sunday lunches (for which booking is advisable), and a wide range of home made desserts which include treacle tart, lemon meringue roulade, strawberry meringue nests and mango and cointreau trifle. The Full Cream Tea of two scones (one fruit, one plain), jams, clotted cream and tea or coffee is reasonably priced at £3.20, and there is a full range of teas, served in crockery teapots, not stainless steel, and a selection of herbal teas.

Hours of business:
December to March - open weekends only 10am to 5pm
March to June - open daily 10am to 5pm except Tuesdays
July to September - open daily 10am to 6pm
October - open daily 10am to 5pm except Tuesdays
November - closed.

The Willows
5 Blandford Road   Disabled Access
Shillingstone   Parking - on premises
Blandford Forum
Dorset
DT11 0SG   Tel: 01258 861167

Set on the eastern side of the village of Shillingstone on the A357, there is lovely walking and cycling to be enjoyed near to The Willows on Wessex Ridgeway. The building itself is an eighteenth century cob and brick cottage with inglenook fireplace. Located at the foot of scenic Hambledon Hill, on the Wessex Ridgeway, Shillingstone is just five miles from Blandford Forum, an interesting and historic Georgian town.

The Dorset Cream Tea supplies two home made scones with strawberry jam, butter, clotted cream and a pot of tea. Farmhouse Tea consists of a boiled egg with wholemeal bread and butter, a choice of cake from the display cabinet and a pot of tea. These are both reasonably priced at £2.90 and £2.50 respectively.

Cakes and scones are home made and one favourite out of the variety on offer is the Dorset Apple Cake, which is served with clotted cream. Teas on offer include Ceylon, Darjeeling and Earl Grey.

Hours of business:
March to end of October - Tuesdays to Sundays 10am to 6pm
November and December - open weekends only
January - closed
February - open weekends only.

The Parlour
112 East Street   Disabled Access
South Molton   Parking - within 50m
Devon
EX36 3DB   Tel: 01769 574144

The Parlour Tea Room, a beautiful Georgian building in the market town of South Molton, is situated next to the garage and close to Quince Honey Farm. Furnished as a 1900s front parlour, with gate leg tables and wheelback chairs, it has an area which sells small antiques. The main local attraction is the breathtaking scenery of Exmoor.

Devonshire Cream Tea is set alongside a wide range of home made cakes and biscuits cooked on the premises. There are several unusual cakes which change from time to time as the menu is constantly updated. Tea is loose leaf and there are nine different types, including Assam, Darjeeling, Earl Grey, Keemun, Lapsang Souchong, Rose Hip and Camomile. There is also a good selection of soft drinks and other hot beverages.

Hours of business:
Tuesdays to Saturdays - 10am to 4.30pm.
Closed on Sundays and Mondays.

——— oOo ———

Should I, after tea and cakes and ices,
Have the strength to force the moment to its crisis?

(T.S. Eliot - Portrait of a Lady)

Bumbles Tea Room

Digey Square   Disabled Access
St Ives   Parking - within 100m
Cornwall
TR26 1HR   Tel: 01736 797977

Set near an artists' community, the Tate Gallery and Porthmeor Beach, Bumbles Tea Room is just fifty yards from the Town Centre. It is a typical olde worlde tea room, with floral décor and pretty china, located in old St Ives. Within easy travelling distance are Lands End and Penzance, plus miles of beautiful rocky coastline footpaths.

Specialities include home made cakes and Cornish Cream Teas, these consisting of two home made scones with strawberry jam and clotted cream, and a pot of tea or coffee. Several varieties of tea are on offer, including Assam, China, Ceylon, Darjeeling and Earl Grey. Also available are toasted sandwiches, jacket potatoes and salads, to name just a few items from the menu.

Hours of business:
Mondays to Saturdays - 10am to 5pm
Sundays (during summer months only) - 11am to 4.30pm.

*I could have introduced you to some
very beautiful people. Mrs Langtry and Lady Lonsdale
and a lot of clever beings who were at tea with me.*

(Oscar Wilde - letter to Harold Boulton 1879)

Four and Twenty Blackbirds
43 Gold Street
Tiverton   Parking - within 100m
Devon
EX16 6QB   Tel: 01884 257055

At the bottom of Lowman Green Clock Tower, these tea rooms are set below kerb level in an area known as The Pound. Old beams and a motley assortment of furniture and objets d'art enhance the traditional atmosphere.

Fresh flowers decorate the rooms and an old range with a gas coal fire warms the main seating area. Antiques are for sale upstairs and there is a warm, friendly atmosphere throughout.

Local attractions include Tiverton Castle, and the Great Western Canal, plus the town of Tiverton itself.

A wide range of goodies on the menu include Cream Tea, Queens Tea, Kings Tea and Blackbirds Tea, each offering something a little different. Unusual speciality cakes are available, all completely home baked. Among the teas are Ceylon, Darjeeling, Earl Grey, Lapsang Souchong and various herb teas.

Hours of business:
Open all year - 9am to 5pm.

Georgian Tea Room

Broadway House
35 High Street
Topsham
Devon
EX3 0ED

Disabled assistance
Parking - within 50m

Tel: 01392 873465

The Georgian Tea Room is set in a lovely old town where many of the houses are of Dutch origin. Nearby is ideal birdwatching country and the Quay Antique Centre. Built in 1777, the Georgian Grade II listed building has a very fine staircase, and the hall contains 16th and 17th century embossed Spanish leather panels. In the summer guests can enjoy their tea in a walled, secluded garden.

The tables in the Tea Room are covered with embroidered cloths and set with fresh flowers. The proprietor Heather Knee has won the Heartbeat Award for the 5th year, and the tea room appears in two Egon Ronay guides.

Cakes, 'scrummy' scones and jams are home made and served on pretty bone china. The wide range of teas includes Assam, Ceylon, China, Rose Pouchong, Lapsang Souchong, Jasmine and decaffeinated. The food is prepared on the premises to a very high standard, and traditional methods and fresh local produce are used whenever possible.

An extensive lunch menu is offered, and hot and cold food is served all day. A range of desserts and ices are available, and for those who ask, there are 'Slimmers Desserts'.

Hours of business:
Daily - 9.30am to 5pm including Bank Holidays.
Closed for four days over Christmas.

Tawnys
86 Fore Street   Disabled Access
Topsham   Parking - within 50m
Exeter
Devon
EX3 0HQ   Tel: 01392 877887

Tawny's tea rooms are situated opposite Matthews Hall and Car Park in the centre of the town. Inside Tawny's, the proprietor, Dee McNeish, offers a range of local craft items and paintings. The atmosphere is very friendly and homely, epitomising the English tea room. Around Topsham, while away the hours birdwatching, lounging at the outdoor swimming pool or browsing through the antique shops.

Afternoon Tea with a slice of home made cake, or the Devon Cream Tea with two home baked scones, Devon clotted cream and jam are reasonably priced and bread comes from the local baker.

There is a good selection of teas, including Assam, Ceylon, China, Darjeeling and Earl Grey and these are supplemented with London Herb and Spice Company Teas. Light lunches, daily specials and Wednesday roasts are also available.

Hours of business:
Mondays to Fridays   9.30am to 4.45pm
Saturdays - 8.30am to 4.45pm
Closed on Sundays and Bank Holidays.

The Tudor Rose Tea Rooms & Restaurant
14 Victoria Parade
Torquay   Parking - within 50m
Devon
TQ1 2BB   Tel: 01803 296558

Overlooking the harbour and marina, The Tudor Rose is an historic building close to Cockington, the model village and Kent's Cavern. Also in the locality are Paignton Zoo and Torre Abbey.

The interior of the tea rooms was featured in an article in The Times in 1993; the Tudor style décor with oak panelling, oak tables and chairs creates an olde worlde atmosphere in this Grade II listed building. For the warmer days, tables and chairs with umbrellas are set outside the shop.

Cream Teas are served with scones and a variety of cakes, all home made. Two scones, served with jam and cream, and pot of tea is available for just £3.10. Also available is a wide range of ice cream specialities and the teas include Assam, Ceylon, China, Darjeeling and Earl Grey.

Hours of business:
Winter opening - 10.30am to 5.30pm
Summer opening - 10.30am to 10pm.

——— oOo ———

Retired to their tea and scandal,
according to their ancient custom.

(William Congreve)

Greys Dining Room
96 High Street   Disabled Access
Totnes   Parking - within 100m
Devon
TQ9 5SN   Tel: 01803 866369

Situated in The Narrows, Totnes's most interesting part of the High Street, and opposite the post office, Greys Dining Room has a Georgian façade with two display windows, each housing a magnificent fern in an urn. One wall of the shop has original wood panels, discovered by the present owners under another wall.

The cake display cabinet is Flemish in origin and there are collections of copper, blue and white china and saucers. Tea is served in silver-plated teapots and the entrance to the kitchen is behind a Victorian decoupaged screen.

Cream Tea offers home made scones, two types of jam, clotted cream and a pot of tea. Totnes Tea serves two hot toasted crumpets, a dish of cheddar cheese and a pot of tea or cup of coffee. All of the delicious cakes are home baked and there is a choice of thirty seven different teas and infusions.

Local attractions include the Norman castle, the 14th century Church, the medieval town layout and the River Dart.

Hours of business:
Mondays, Tuesdays, Thursdays, Saturdays - 10am to 5pm
Fridays - 9.30am to 5pm
Sundays - 2 - 5pm
Closed on Wednesdays.

Stable Cottage Tea Rooms

Stable Cottage   Disabled Access
Triscombe   Parking - on premises
Nr Taunton
Somerset
TA4 3HG   Tel: 01984 618239

Stable Cottage Tea Rooms are set in proprietor Susan Bucknall's own grounds, with magnificent views of the Quantock Hills. It is off the A358 Taunton to Minehead road between the villages of West Bagborough and Crowcombe in the hamlet of Triscombe. Local attractions include the Quantock Hills and West Somerset Railway.

Stable Cottage was once the stable yard to Triscombe House. Teas are served in the original wood panelled harness rooms which still retain the original atmosphere, and are full of family and country sports pictures. Log fires give a warming welcome in the winter. There is also a spacious conservatory which looks out over the lovely gardens. When the weather permits, teas are also served in the gardens, where well behaved children and dogs on leads are welcome.

The range of set Afternoon Teas is excellent and include, Triscombe Special with a boiled or poached free range egg, toast, jam, two scones, clotted cream and a pot of tea or coffee for £5.25. Also available is a Cream Tea for £3.00 and a Farmhouse Tea for £4.75, plus an extensive selection of speciality teas, herbal tea, coffee and cold beverages. For a summer treat, try the Cricketer Real Dairy Ice Cream!

Hours of business:
Open every afternoon from pre-Easter week until end October - 2pm to 5.30pm.
Open weekends throughout winter.
Open for Sunday lunches throughout the year.

Cherry Garden Tea Room
Carnon Down Garden Centre
Carnon Down   Parking   on premises
Truro
Cornwall

                                 Tel: 01872 865937

Situated in one of Cornwall's main garden centres, four miles from Truro city centre, the Cherry Garden Tea Room is close to the National Trust Garden at Trelissick, the River Fal Estuary and the Cornish coast. At the rear of the detached premises is a lawned garden available to customers for dining when the weather permits.

The full Cornish Cream Tea offered by the proprietors, William and Carol Spurway, consists of two home made scones (plain or fruit), with Cornish clotted cream, strawberry jam and tea for one. All the bread and cakes are also home baked. Among the teas on offer are Assam, Ceylon, Darjeeling and Earl Grey.

Hours of business:
Closed Easter Sunday and Christmas.

Tea! thou soft, thou sober, sage and venerable liquid...
thou female tongue-running, smile smoothing, heart-opening,
wink-tippling
cordial, to whose glorious insipidity I owe the happiest moment of
my life, let me fall prostrate.

(Colley Cibber - The Lady's Last Stake)

Vellow Tea Gardens
Vellow   Disabled Access
Stogumber   Parking - on premises
Nr Williton
Somerset
TA4 4LS   Tel: 01984 656411

Amid wonderful walking country, the Tea Gardens are set in an acre of lushly planted garden, with a wide fast flowing stream running through, with tumbling willows, flowering shrubs and an abundance of flowers, giving an air of quietness and tranquillity. The proprietor, Ann Bryant, began to plan this beautiful garden some thirty years ago and, as well as the tea guests, it draws a great variety of birds and wildlife. It is located off the A358 between Minehead and Taunton.

If the weather should be inclement, there is a cosy indoor tea room with views over the garden. In the locality, you will find Vellow Pottery, Bee World and West Somerset Steam Railway. Next to the Tea Garden is Ann's floral art studio.

Beautifully presented food such as scones and tea cakes, are all served in covered baskets, having been baked on the premises in the Aga. Specialities include home made cheese and herb scones, Old Fashioned Bread Pudding, Treacle Tart, cakes and quiches. And for a special summer time treat, try the Vellow Tea Garden Special, Tequila Sundae which is a delicious combination of vanilla ice cream, fresh fruit, raspberry sauce, laced with Tequila. Scrumptious!

As they say, this is "A truly English Tea Garden" and a perfect place for tea!

Hours of business:
Open every day - 10.30am to 5.30pm.
Last orders taken at 5pm.

INDEX by Tea Room

203

INDEX In order of Town

206

YOU CAN HELP ....

Sadly, in this book it is just not possible to cover every good tea room in every town or village. However, if you have a particular favourite, or have any comments about the current establishments featured herein, I'd be delighted to hear from you. Please contact me at:

Whitehill Publishing
2 Ennel Copse
North Baddesley
Southampton
United Kingdom
SO52 9LB

M.T.